Horizons

Pre-Algebra
Tests and Resources

Author:

Shelly Chittam, M.S.

Managing Editor:

Alan Christopherson, M.S.

Editors:

Laura Messner, B.A.
Rachelle Wiersma, M.A.

Graphic Design & Illustration:

Ron A. Hartmann, B.A.

Alpha Omega Publications, Inc. • Rock Rapids, IA

Pre-Algebra

Tests and Resources

Contents

Course Introduction

The *Horizons Pre-Algebra Tests and Resources Book* is a consumable component that is to be used with the Horizons Pre-Algebra course. This book should be kept by the teacher and the pages should be passed out as they are called for in the Teacher's Guide Lesson Plan. By providing the tests and worksheets in a separate book the opportunity is reduced for the student to see these materials before they are distributed which will increase the validity of the assessment results. Each item should be removed from this book prior to distribution. The pages are perforated for easy removal.

This book includes the following:

Tests—There are 16 tests in the Horizons Pre-Algebra course. One test follows each set of 10 lessons.

Exams—Four exams have been developed for this course. One exam follows every 40 lessons. Exam 4 is also a final exam. You have the option of administering the first two pages as a fourth quarter exam, or all six pages as a cumulative final exam.

Worksheets—This course has 80 worksheets. These worksheets have been developed for reinforcement and drill. A complete listing of the worksheets and where they might best be used is provided on the following pages or in the Teacher's Guide. Some Worksheets are for additional practice of a new concept while others are for review or a quiz grade. The Lesson Plan will indicate which case applies for each Worksheet.

Formula Strips—Occasionally, formula strips are called for in this course. Students should cut these out when the Lesson Plan calls for them. The number of formulas and conversion factors that the students must memorize has been limited to the ones that are typically required by standardized testing.

Nets Supplements—This course includes supplements for the lessons that cover nets of 3-D shapes. Students should cut these out when the Lesson Plan calls for them. Details on their use are given in the Lesson Plans where needed.

Algebra Tiles—Algebra tiles will be used in this course. The students should cut these out the first time the Lesson Plan calls for them, and store them in a zip-top bag for future use. These manipulatives will assist both visual and kinesthetic learners in mastering algebraic concepts.

Where To Use *Pre-Algebra Worksheets*

In the Tests and Resources book you will find eighty worksheets.
This chart shows where worksheets may be used for *Horizons Pre-Algebra*.

Where To Use Pre-Algebra Worksheets, continued:

1 Identify each number as *natural*, *whole*, *integer*, *rational*, *irrational*, or *real*. Some numbers may have more than one answer. **24 points**

	68	$-\sqrt{5}$	$2\frac{3}{8}$	-3	46.66	π	$\frac{5}{9}$	-0.07
Natural								
Whole								
Integer								
Rational								
Irrational								
Real								

2 Estimate the sum by rounding to the nearest thousand. **4 points**

$$\begin{array}{r} 2903 \\ +1102 \\ \hline \end{array} \approx \qquad \begin{array}{r} 7987 \\ +2019 \\ \hline \end{array} \approx \qquad \begin{array}{r} 4176 \\ +8885 \\ \hline \end{array} \approx \qquad \begin{array}{r} 3997 \\ +4009 \\ \hline \end{array} \approx$$

3 Estimate each product by rounding to the nearest ten. **4 points**

21 x 128 ≈ _____

67 x 32 ≈ _____

58 x 61 ≈ _____

52 x 48 ≈ _____

4 Solve, using the rules for signed numbers. **14 points**

(+48) + (+4) =   (+99) + (-72) =

(-2) + (+24) =   (+35) − (+71) =

(-3) − (-34) =   (-18) − (+82) =

(9)(11) =   (-6)(40) =

(5)(-6) =   (10)(13)(-1) =

(-9)(4) =   (-11)(8)(-1) =

(-3)(-20) =   (-5)(-12)(-1) =

5 Solve, using the rules of absolute values. **10 points**

$|-2| + |-75| =$ $|97| - |93| =$

$|-3| + |56| =$ $-|-21| - |-18| =$

$|75| - |-9| =$ $|8 + 2| + |23 - 6| =$

$-|12| + |-4| =$ $-|16 - 2| + |6 - 9| =$

$-|79| - |-1| =$ $-|27 + 3| - |61 - 9| =$

6 Find all of the natural number factors for each of the following numbers.

12 _____

15 _____

18 _____

20 _____

21 _____

24 _____

7 Write 5 multiples of each of the following numbers.   **25 points**

7 _____

10 _____

11 _____

15 _____

20 _____

8 Solve.   **20 points**

$$
\begin{array}{r} 85419 \\ +13602 \\ \hline \end{array}
\qquad
\begin{array}{r} 64106 \\ +12925 \\ \hline \end{array}
\qquad
\begin{array}{r} 88873 \\ +97381 \\ \hline \end{array}
\qquad
\begin{array}{r} 72945 \\ +34994 \\ \hline \end{array}
\qquad
\begin{array}{r} 17811 \\ +62835 \\ \hline \end{array}
$$

$$
\begin{array}{r} 15433 \\ -10662 \\ \hline \end{array}
\qquad
\begin{array}{r} 48738 \\ -34154 \\ \hline \end{array}
\qquad
\begin{array}{r} 86476 \\ -75093 \\ \hline \end{array}
\qquad
\begin{array}{r} 18754 \\ -13354 \\ \hline \end{array}
\qquad
\begin{array}{r} 93312 \\ -50873 \\ \hline \end{array}
$$

$$
\begin{array}{r} 177 \\ \times 92 \\ \hline \end{array}
\qquad
\begin{array}{r} 435 \\ \times 35 \\ \hline \end{array}
\qquad
\begin{array}{r} 812 \\ \times 96 \\ \hline \end{array}
\qquad
\begin{array}{r} 646 \\ \times 15 \\ \hline \end{array}
\qquad
\begin{array}{r} 688 \\ \times 55 \\ \hline \end{array}
$$

$$
94\overline{)658} \qquad 44\overline{)132} \qquad 66\overline{)264} \qquad 42\overline{)588} \qquad 33\overline{)561}
$$

135 points total

Horizons Pre-Algebra; Tests and Resources

1 Use the divisibility tests to tell if 2, 3, 4, 5, 6, and 9 are factors of each number.   **19 points**

	90	91	92	93	94	95	96	115	116	117
2										
3										
4										
5										
6										
9										

2 Identify each number as prime or composite.   **10 points**

2 _____   11 _____

3 _____   13 _____

4 _____   15 _____

5 _____   19 _____

7 _____   21 _____

3 Express the prime factorization of each number using exponents.   **9 points**

12	16	18
20	24	25
28	32	36

4 Find the square of each number.   **10 points**

2 _____   9 _____

3 _____   10 _____

5 _____ .   11 _____

6 _____   12 _____

8 _____   13 _____

5 Solve, following the order of operations.

$5 + 3 \times 8 =$

$8 \div (2 + 6) + 1 =$

$3 - (7 + 2) + 9 =$

$8^2 - 3^2 \times 4 =$

$4 \times 3^2 - 6 \times 4 =$

$3^2 - 4^2 \div 8 - 7 =$

$5^2 \times (4 - 6^2 \div 9) =$

$2 \times (3^2 + 1) - 5 \times 2 =$

$5 + (1 - 2^2) + 8 =$

$2 \times 7 - (5 - 2 - 6) =$

6 Find the greatest common factor of each set of numbers. **6 points**

12 and 15   16 and 24   9 and 12

20 and 32   27 and 45   28 and 42

7 Find the least common multiple of each set of numbers. **6 points**

6 and 9   10 and 15   12 and 18

12 and 20   15 and 25   16 and 24

70 points total

1 Simplify the roots.

$\sqrt{36} =$

$6\sqrt[3]{5} - 2\sqrt[3]{5} =$

$\sqrt{27} =$

$\left(\sqrt{8}\right)\left(\sqrt{2}\right) =$

$\sqrt{18} =$

$\left(\sqrt{3}\right)\left(2\sqrt{15}\right) =$

$\sqrt[3]{8} =$

$\sqrt{48} \div \sqrt{3} =$

$\sqrt[3]{64} =$

$6\sqrt{24} \div 3\sqrt{8} =$

$\sqrt{11} + 4\sqrt{11} =$

$7 \div \sqrt{7} =$

2 Translate the following words into a mathematical expression. Do not solve. **10 points**

The product of 5 and a number _____

The ratio of a number to 8 _____

A number increased by 31 _____

The total of a number and 28 is 61. _____

8 fewer than a number equals 3. _____

A number times 7 yields 42. _____

The sum of 16 and a number is 29. _____

6 less than a number is 19. _____

A number increased by a factor of 4 gives 32. _____

51 more than a number is 88. _____

3 Solve. **6 points**

$x + 6 + 5 = 18$

$x + 3x + 3 + 7 = 26$

$2x + 3x + 6 - 1 = 20$

$3x + x - 9 + 4 = 31$

$5x - 2x + 11 - 4 - 1 = 24$

$6x + 2x - x - 8 - 4 + 1 = 38$

4 Solve the inequalities. **6 points**

$4x < 12$

$3x + 11 > 17$

$3x - 8 < x + 14$

$-5x < 15$

$2x + 7 > x - 3$

$7x + 9 < 3x + 1$

5 Solve.

19.67	39.51	694.57	519.4	457.09
+65.34	+27.64	+183.82	+73.38	+256.8

39.974	234.74	692.5	198.72	567.23
−16.237	−56.19	−47.23	−9.999	−92.3745

2.9	7.3	.33	7.8	.48
×.8	×6.1	×8.3	×.66	×.13

$1.8\overline{)1.62}$ $1.6\overline{)2.56}$ $.14\overline{)1.96}$ $.15\overline{)1.35}$ $.16\overline{)20.8}$

6 Write < or > for each pair of decimals.

6 points

314.954 _____ 413.459   648.815 _____ 648.9

92.763 _____ 92.673   35.743 _____ 35.753

21.89 _____ 21.91   800.003 _____ 800.0007

7 Solve.

8 points

$10^4 =$ $10^{-6} =$

$10^7 =$ $10^{-8} =$

$(10^3)(10^6) =$ $(10^7)(10^{-5}) =$

$(10^{12}) \div (10^5) =$ $(10^4) \div (10^{-1}) =$

8 Write an equation and solve.

2 points

Four teenagers each worked 5 hours in Billy's concession stand on Saturday. If the concession stand made $115.80 profit, was there enough profit to pay each teenager $5 per hour toward youth activity fees? If so, how much extra was there? If not, how much money are they short?

70 points total

1 Solve.

$5 \times 10^0 =$

$0.7 \times 10^1 =$

$0.36 \times 10^2 =$

$9.42 \times 10^3 =$

$9.54 \times 10^0 =$

$0.816 \times 10^1 =$

$94.5 \times 10^2 =$

$0.071 \times 10^3 =$

$8.17 \times 10^0 =$

$0.352 \times 10^{-1} =$

$46.87 \times 10^{-2} =$

$0.0079 \times 10^{-3} =$

$5.19 \div 10^0 =$

$18.38 \div 10^1 =$

$6.21 \div 10^2 =$

$99.26 \div 10^3 =$

$13.92 \div 10^0 =$

$5.63 \div 10^1 =$

$3.91 \div 10^2 =$

$2.61 \div 10^3 =$

$0.048 \div 10^0 =$

$0.61 \div 10^{-1} =$

$0.09 \div 10^{-2} =$

$1.3 \div 10^{-3} =$

2 Multiply or divide the appropriate powers of 10 to complete the metric conversions.

8 points

10 kg = _____ g

0.4 km = _____ m

3.2 kL = _____ L

62.46 kW = _____ W

9000 g = _____ kg

8163 L = _____ kL

266 m = _____ km

54.1 W = _____ kW

3 Multiply or divide the appropriate powers of 10 to complete the metric conversions.

8 points

13 g = _____ cg

0.6 m = _____ mm

1.4 L = _____ cL

54.19 W = _____ mW

2000 cg = _____ g

8168 mL = _____ L

357 cm = _____ m

8.19 mW = _____ W

4 Solve the numerators to make equivalent fractions.

6 points

$\dfrac{1}{4} = \dfrac{}{12}$

$\dfrac{2}{3} = \dfrac{}{12}$

$\dfrac{1}{4} = \dfrac{}{20}$

$\dfrac{3}{4} = \dfrac{}{16}$

$\dfrac{2}{5} = \dfrac{}{25}$

$\dfrac{1}{6} = \dfrac{}{24}$

5 Write the following fractions as decimals.   **8 points**

$\dfrac{1}{2} =$ $\dfrac{3}{4} =$ $\dfrac{5}{6} =$ $\dfrac{1}{3} =$

$\dfrac{1}{6} =$ $\dfrac{2}{5} =$ $\dfrac{3}{8} =$ $\dfrac{4}{5} =$

6 Write the following decimals as fractions.   **8 points**

$0.25 =$ $0.625 =$ $0.7 =$ $0.6 =$

$0.\overline{6} =$ $0.4 =$ $0.2 =$ $0.3 =$

7 Add, subtract, multiply, or divide as indicated.   **20 points**

$\dfrac{1}{5} + \dfrac{3}{5} =$ $\dfrac{2}{5} \times \dfrac{1}{5} =$

$\dfrac{1}{7} + \dfrac{4}{7} =$ $\dfrac{4}{5} \times \dfrac{3}{8} =$

$\dfrac{1}{3} + \dfrac{1}{6} =$ $\dfrac{5}{7} \times \dfrac{7}{10} =$

$\dfrac{1}{4} + \dfrac{3}{8} =$ $\dfrac{5}{8} \times \dfrac{1}{2} =$

$\dfrac{5}{8} + \dfrac{1}{12} =$ $\dfrac{5}{8} \times \dfrac{4}{5} =$

$\dfrac{4}{5} - \dfrac{3}{5} =$ $\dfrac{2}{5} \div \dfrac{1}{5} =$

$\dfrac{2}{3} - \dfrac{1}{6} =$ $\dfrac{3}{8} \div \dfrac{1}{8} =$

$\dfrac{9}{10} - \dfrac{3}{4} =$ $\dfrac{4}{7} \div \dfrac{2}{3} =$

$\dfrac{7}{9} - \dfrac{2}{3} =$ $\dfrac{5}{8} \div \dfrac{3}{4} =$

$\dfrac{5}{8} - \dfrac{1}{4} =$ $\dfrac{3}{8} \div \dfrac{9}{10} =$

82 points total

     Horizons Pre-Algebra, Tests and Resources

1 Add, subtract, multiply, or divide as indicated. Convert answers with improper fractions to mixed numbers if the problem has mixed numbers. **16 points**

$$\frac{5}{2} + \frac{9}{5} =$$

$$\frac{8}{5} \times \frac{9}{4} =$$

$$3\frac{1}{8} + 2\frac{3}{5} =$$

$$2\frac{1}{3} \times 3\frac{4}{7} =$$

$$\frac{7}{4} - \frac{8}{5} =$$

$$\frac{13}{4} \div \frac{5}{2} =$$

$$5\frac{3}{5} - 3\frac{1}{3} =$$

$$4\frac{1}{3} \div 3\frac{1}{4} =$$

2 Set up a proper conversion formula and calculate the equivalent length for each given length. **16 points**

3 miles	yards
4 miles	feet
5 yards	inches
39 feet	yards
10 inches	cm
12 inches	mm
11 yards	meters
6 miles	km

3 Write ratios in simplest form. **6 points**
A band has 25 clarinets, 20 flutes, 15 saxophones, 10 oboes, and 5 bassoons in the woodwind section.

What is the ratio of flutes to oboes?

What is the ratio of oboes to saxophones?

What is the ratio of bassoons to flutes?

What is the ratio of clarinets to oboes?

What is the ratio of oboes and bassoons to clarinets and flutes?

What is the ratio of clarinets to all woodwinds?

4 Write = or ≠ to indicate if each pair of ratios forms a proportion. **4 points**

$$\frac{39}{51} \quad \frac{13}{17}$$

$$\frac{11}{15} \quad \frac{7}{11}$$

$$\frac{4}{24} \quad \frac{6}{36}$$

$$\frac{15}{35} \quad \frac{3}{7}$$

5 Solve the proportions.

$$\frac{x}{8} = \frac{24}{6}$$ $$\frac{9}{21} = \frac{x}{112}$$ $$\frac{15}{x} = \frac{25}{15}$$ $$\frac{4}{9} = \frac{36}{x}$$

6 Label the scale drawing if the ratio of the scale drawing to the actual measurements is 1:3. **6 points**

Actual measurements

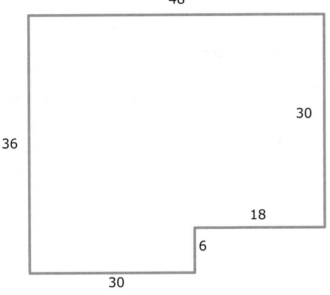

Scale drawing measurements

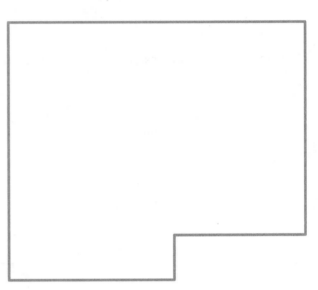

7 Write each number in scientific notation.   **8 points**

320,000,000   0.000000375

97,000,000   0.00089

4,180,000,000   0.0000007612

6,000,000   0.000000001

8 Convert each percent to a decimal.   **6 points**

17%   32%

80%   314%

66%   200%

9 Convert each decimal to a percent.   **6 points**

0.88   7.6

0.07   9.15

0.31   6

64 points total

1 Solve.

What is 45% of 80?　　　32 is 40% of what number?　　　75 is what percent of 125?

What is 0.36% of 600?　　　33 is 0.55% of what number?　　　5 is what percent of 1250?

2 Complete the fraction-percent conversions. **16 points**

Fraction	Percent
	25%
	$33.\overline{3}\%$
	20%
	10%
	60%
	$83.\overline{3}\%$
	62.5%
	87.5%

Percent	Fraction
	$\dfrac{2}{3}$
	$\dfrac{2}{5}$
	$\dfrac{1}{6}$
	$\dfrac{1}{8}$
	$\dfrac{3}{4}$
	$\dfrac{3}{10}$
	$\dfrac{7}{10}$
	$\dfrac{3}{8}$

3 Complete the chart. **6 points**

Original price	Discount	Sale price
$50	70%	
$120		$75
$90	40%	
$144		$120
$45	30%	
$75		$50

4 Complete the chart. **6 points**

Original price	Mark-up	New price
$50	50%	
$120		$150
$90	30%	
$144		$168
$45	80%	
$75		$100

5 Complete the chart to reflect simple interest. **10 points**

Principal	Interest rate	Time in years	Amount of interest	Total amount paid
$1000	4%	3		
$5000	6%	5		
$10,000	8%	7		
$15,000	10%	9		
$20,000	12%	11		

6 Solve. **5 points**

A real estate agent charges 7% commission for selling a house. If you offer a $5000 reward to the person who refers a buyer for you to sell your house yourself, what percent are you paying as a reward if you sell your house for $125,000? What would the real estate agent have charged you had you listed the house with the agent? How much money would you save by selling the house yourself?

If you purchased the home for $99,500 and sold it for $125,000, how much profit did you make if you paid a $5000 reward to the person finding a buyer for your house?

A musician is paid royalties as follows: 10% of the selling price of a CD for each of the first 10,000 CDs sold; 20% of the selling price for each of the next 10,000 CDs sold, and 30% of the selling price for each CD sold over 20,000. If a musician sells 50,000 CDs for $15 each, what will the musician earn in royalties?

49 points total

1 Use the formula $A = P(1 + r)^t$ to calculate compound interest.　　**10 points**

Initial principal	Interest rate	Time in years	Total compounded annually	Total compounded quarterly
$100	3%	3		
$500	7%	3		
$1000	10%	5		
$5,000	15%	10		
$10,000	24%	10		

2 Solve.　　**3 points**

What is 350% of 700?　　What is 375% of 450?　　What is 248.9% of 400?

3 Draw a pictograph to show the number of rows for each number of seats.　　**6 points**

The theater Duane performs in has 12 rows with 14 seats each, 27 rows with 8 seats each, 8 rows with 7 seats each, and 7 rows with 6 seats each.

4 Draw a circle graph.

The theater Duane performs in has 12 rows with 14 seats each, 27 rows with 8 seats each, 8 rows with 7 seats each, and 7 rows with 6 seats each.

5 Make a frequency distribution and find the mean, median, and mode. **15 points**

The results of 20 rolls of a die are 1, 3, 6, 2, 3, 1, 2, 6, 1, 1, 5, 2, 5, 2, 5, 6, 2, 4, 4, 2. Round answers to the nearest tenth where appropriate.

6 Make a stem-and-leaf plot and find the range. **11 points**

The points scored by 30 college football teams in bowl games are as follows: 35, 28, 45, 24, 42, 32, 45, 10, 17, 21, 21, 13, 44, 20, 21, 30, 43, 42, 47, 20, 13, 35, 14, 13, 38, 35, 17, 20, 41, 31.

51 points total

1 For each set of numbers, draw a histogram, list the 5-number summary, and draw a box-and-whisker plot.

14 points

50, 53, 64, 69, 90, 52, 24, 18, 47, 16, 84, 70, 69, 20, 36, 38, 68, 26, 49, 88

60, 58, 23, 65, 48, 54, 46, 76, 66, 39, 48, 60, 63, 43, 78, 56, 12, 60, 62, 42, 51, 59, 77, 52, 83

2 Draw a line graph.

14 points

Draw a line graph showing the average low temperatures in Honolulu. The average low temperature, in degrees Fahrenheit, for each month is as follows: January: 66, February: 65, March: 67, April: 68, May: 70, June: 72, July: 74, August: 75, September: 74, October: 73, November: 71, December: 68.

3 Complete the chart to show probability and odds.

12 points

Scenario	Number of Possible Outcomes	Desired Event (E)	P(E)	Odds (in Favor of E)	Odds (Against E)
Flip a coin once		Heads			
Roll a 6-sided die once		Odd number			
Choose an integer from 1 to 10		Prime number			

4 Calculate the permutations and combinations.

p(7,3) =   C(7,3) =

p(4,2) =   C(4,2) =

p(6,3) =   C(6,3) =

p(8,2) =   C(8,2) =

5 Solve.

A card game has 4 different colors of cards and 14 different numbers on the cards. How many combinations are possible with one color and one number?

A school has 3 different choices for shirt color, 2 different choices for pant color, and 3 different choices for sweater color for the school uniform. How many different uniform combinations are possible?

You roll 5 dice at one time. What is the probability that you will roll a 4 on all 5 dice?

If you rolled a 6 on 2 of the dice in your first roll, what is the probability that you will roll a 6 with your three remaining dice in your second roll?

6 Follow the directions.

It takes a minimum of 270 electoral votes to win the presidency. Draw a bar graph showing the number of electoral votes each of the past 7 presidents won. If a president won a second term, only the electoral votes for his second term are listed.
Barack Obama: 365
George W. Bush: 286
Bill Clinton: 379
George H.W. Bush: 426
Ronald Reagan: 525
Jimmy Carter: 297
Richard Nixon: 301

61 points total

1 Complete the chart.

Figure	Drawing	Symbol
	•T	
		$\overleftrightarrow{PQ}$
Segment *JK*		
		$\overrightarrow{AB}$
	F∠	
Parallel lines *m* and *n*		

2 Find the perimeter and area of each figure in the chart below.

Figure	Perimeter	Area
$3\frac{1}{3}$ in. / $1\frac{3}{4}$ in.		
2.1cm / 2.1cm		
4.3m / 6.1m / 10.2 m		
$2\sqrt{3}$ yd. / $2\sqrt{6}$ yd. / $2\sqrt{3}$ yd. / $2\sqrt{15}$ yd. / $6\sqrt{3}$ yd. / $2\sqrt{3}$ yd.		

3 Complete the chart for circles.

Radius	Diameter	Circumference	Area
5 inches			
	14 cm		
1.5 ft.			
$2\frac{1}{2}$ m			
	$2\sqrt{3}$ yd.		

4 Answer the questions using the diagrams below.   **7 points**

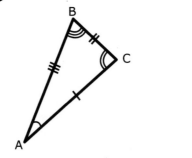
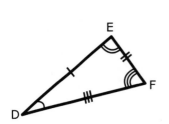

Write a congruence statement for the triangles shown above.

List all pairs of congruent angles.

List all pairs of congruent sides.

5 Find the probabilities.   **3 points**

When a standard six-sided game die is rolled one time, what is the probability that it will be a 2 or a 5?

When a standard six-sided game die is rolled twice, what is the probability that the first roll will be a 2 and the second roll will be a 5?

A set of double-six dominoes has 28 dominoes. If you randomly select two dominoes, what is the probability of drawing the double 2 and the double 5?

45 points total

1 Draw 6 lines of symmetry in the figure below.

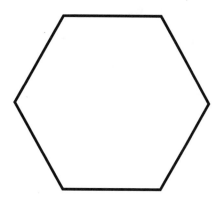

2 Identify whether or not each pair of triangles is congruent based on the information given. If the triangles are congruent, write a congruence statement and tell which congruence pattern applies.

8 points

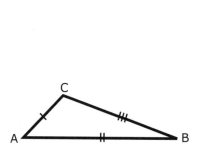

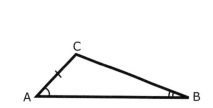

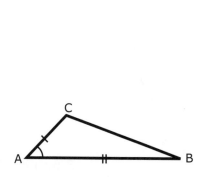

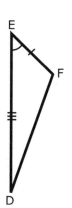

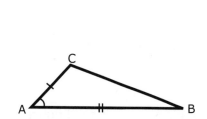

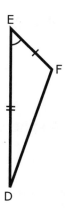

3 Give the number of faces, edges, and vertices in each solid figure.　　**18 points**

Sides on a base	Number of bases	Faces	Edges	Vertices
3	1			
3	2			
5	1			
5	2			
6	1			
6	2			

4 Find the lateral area, surface area, and volume of each solid figure.　　**14 points**

A prism with a height of 9 feet and a rectangular base that is 8 feet long and 3 feet wide.

A pyramid with a height of 6 meters, a slant height of 10 meters, and a square base that is 16 meters on each side.

A cylinder with a height of 8 inches and a base that has a diameter of 3 inches.

A cone with a height of 12 yards, a slant height of 13 yards, and a base that has a diameter of 10 yards.

A sphere with a diameter of 12 cm.

5 Tell the number of faces in each solid figure.　　**3 points**

Dodecahedron _____

Icosahedron _____

Octahedron _____

49 points total

1 Use the formula $m = \frac{w}{g}$ to find the mass or weight of each item. Round answers to the nearest whole number.

3 points

	Baby	Child	Adult
Mass		31.7 kg	
Weight	35 kg · m/s²		778 kg · m/s²
Gravity	9.8 m/s²	9.8 m/s²	9.8 m/s²

2 Use the formula $d = \frac{m}{v}$ to find the density of each object and identify if it will float in pure water. The density of pure water is 1000 kg/m³.

8 points

Substance	Mass	Volume	Density	Float: Y/N
Cocoa beans	415.1 kg	0.7 m³		
Brick	1979.66 kg	1.03 m³		
Furnace cinders	2008.6 kg	2.2 m³		
Cobalt ore	503.6 kg	0.08 m³		

3 Use the formula $V = \frac{d}{t}$ to find the velocity, distance, or time.

3 points

Velocity	Distance	Time
	605 miles	11 hours
54 miles per hour		2.5 hours
350 miles per hour	840 miles	

4 Identify the types of lines in the diagram below.

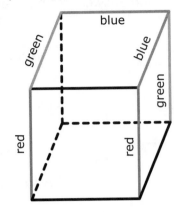

What kind of lines are the blue lines?

What kind of lines are the red lines?

What kind of lines are the green lines?

5 Identify each item in circle *A*.

6 points

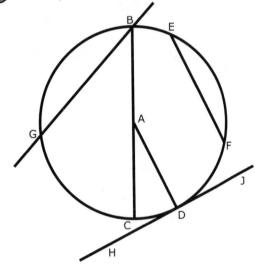

$\overleftrightarrow{BG}$

$\overline{BC}$

$\overline{AD}$

$\overline{EF}$

$\overleftrightarrow{HJ}$

$\angle CAD$

6 Find the measure of each angle in the figure below.

19 points

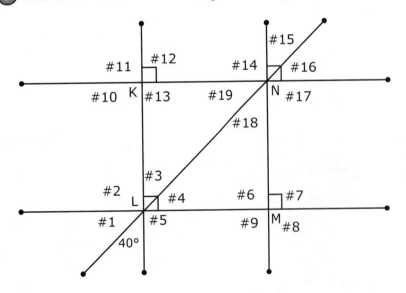

#1 =	#10 =
#2 =	#11 =
#3 =	#12 =
#4 =	#13 =
#5 =	#14 =
#6 =	#15 =
#7 =	#16 =
#8 =	#17 =
#9 =	#18 =
	#19 =

42 points total

1 Graph each point and identify if it is at the origin or in which quadrant it lies.

A. (1, 4)
B. (3, -1)
C. (-2, 3)
D. (-2, -2)
E. (0, 0)

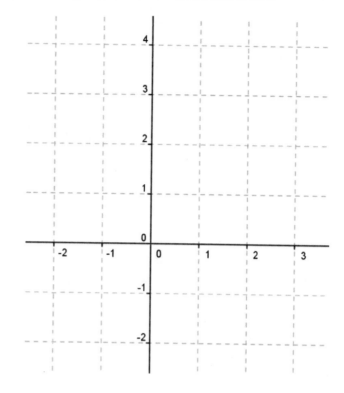

2 Solve each two-variable equation when $x = 4$.

3 points

$y = x + 4$

$y = 2x - 3$

$y = 5(x - 3)$

3 Graph the following equations on your own graph paper.

6 points

$y = -x + 3$

$y = 4x - 1$

$y = 2(3x - 2)$

$y \leq 2(x + 1)$

$y \leq 2x - 3$

$y > x$

4 Tell whether or not each graph is a function.

3 points

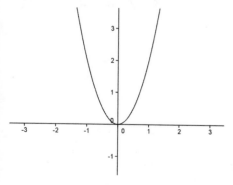

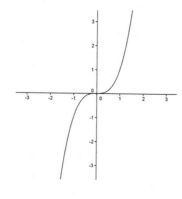

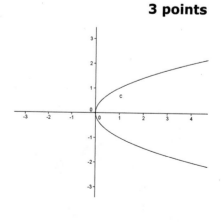

5 Write each equation in slope-intercept form and identify the slope and *y*-intercept.　　**27 points**

$2x + y - 5 = 0$　　　　　　　$3x + y - 4 = 0$　　　　　　　$-7x + y - 3 = 0$

$-3x + y - 4 = 0$　　　　　　$-4x + y + 6 = 0$　　　　　　$8x + y - 9 = 0$

$2x + 2y + 5 = 0$　　　　　　$x + 2y + 6 = 0$　　　　　　　$5x + 2y - 8 = 0$

6 Solve. Express the answer as a coordinate point.　　**6 points**

$x + y + 1 = 0$　　　　　　　$4x - y + 4 = 0$　　　　　　　$3x + y + 5 = 0$
$2x + y - 1 = 0$　　　　　　$-3x + y - 3 = 0$　　　　　　$2x + y - 1 = 0$

$x + 2y - 7 = 0$　　　　　　$3x + 2y + 4 = 0$　　　　　　$2x + 3y + 3 = 0$
$2x + 2y + 3 = 0$　　　　　$2x + 2y - 1 = 0$　　　　　　$2x + y - 1 = 0$

55 points total

1 Complete the chart to show temperature conversions. Round answers to the nearest whole.

14 points

°F	°C		°C	°F
25°			25°	
35°			35°	
45°			45°	
55°			55°	
65°			65°	
75°			75°	
85°			85°	

 2 Solve.

15 points

Convert 18 ounces to milliliters.

Convert 6 quarts to liters.

Convert 25 gallons to liters.

Convert 250 milliliters to ounces.

Convert 8 liters to quarts.

Convert 60 liters to gallons.

Convert 1500 milliliters to quarts.

Convert 125 ounces to liters.

Convert 2500 milliliters to gallons.

Convert 18 ounces to grams.

Convert 48 pounds to kilograms.

Convert 60 S. ton to kilograms.

Convert 250 grams to ounces.

Convert 125 kilograms to pounds.

Convert 2500 M. ton to S. ton.

3 Find the lengths of the missing sides. Then find the sine, cosine, and tangent of each acute angle.

27 points

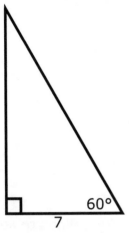

$\sin 30° =$ $\sin 60° =$

$\cos 30° =$ $\cos 60° =$

$\tan 30° =$ $\tan 60° =$

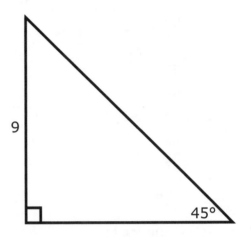

$\sin 45° =$

$\cos 45° =$

$\tan 45° =$

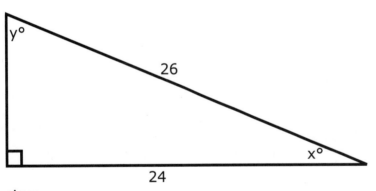

$\sin x =$

$\cos x =$

$\tan x =$

$\sin y =$

$\cos y =$

$\tan y =$

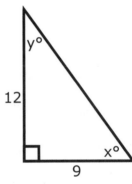

$\sin x =$

$\cos x =$

$\tan x =$

$\sin y =$

$\cos y =$

$\tan y =$

56 points total

1 Add.

$$6x^2 + 7x + 5$$
$$+\ 2x^2 + 3x + 1$$

$$6x^2 + 4x + 3$$
$$+x^2 - 5x - 2$$

$$4x^2 - 2x + 6$$
$$+5x^2 + x - 2$$

$$3x^2 + 4x + 6$$
$$+\ 2x^2 + 7x + 4$$

$$3x^2 + 4x + 8$$
$$+x^2 - 6x - 3$$

$$6x^2 - 7x + 3$$
$$+2x^2 + 4x - 7$$

$$4x^2 + 5x + 2$$
$$+\ 7x^2 + 3x + 8$$

$$2x^2 + 5x + 3$$
$$+x^2 - 7x - 9$$

$$4x^2 - 5x + 3$$
$$+6x^2 + 7x - 8$$

2 Subtract.

9 points

$$\left(7x^2 + 3x + 5\right)$$
$$-\left(3x^2 + 2x + 1\right)$$

$$\left(4x^2 - 6x + 5\right)$$
$$-\left(x^2 - 4x - 1\right)$$

$$\left(3x^2 - 4x - 2\right)$$
$$-\left(5x^2 + 2x - 3\right)$$

$$\left(2x^2 + 4x + 5\right)$$
$$-\left(3x^2 + 2x + 1\right)$$

$$\left(2x^2 - 7x + 6\right)$$
$$-\left(x^2 - 4x - 1\right)$$

$$\left(5x^2 - 1x - 3\right)$$
$$-\left(3x^2 + 2x - 3\right)$$

$$\left(x^2 + 2x + 7\right)$$
$$-\left(4x^2 + 7x + 3\right)$$

$$\left(4x^2 - 7x + 2\right)$$
$$-\left(x^2 - 4x - 1\right)$$

$$\left(2x^2 - 5x - 3\right)$$
$$-\left(5x^2 + 2x - 8\right)$$

3 Identify whether or not each expression is a polynomial. For each polynomial, identify it as a constant, monomial, binomial, or trinomial.

13 points

$9x - 5$

$3x^2 + \frac{7}{x} - 4$

$4x^{-2} + 3$

71

$9x^2 - 5x + 7$

$-2x$

4 Multiply.

$5x\left(7xy^2\right)$ $8x^3\left(5x^2y^2\right)$ $4x\left(2x^2+7x-3\right)$

$8x^2\left(3xy^2\right)$ $9x^3\left(2x^2y^4\right)$ $\left(x+5\right)\left(x-4\right)$

$x^3\left(6xy^2\right)$ $4x\left(2x^2+6x-9\right)$ $\left(2x+1\right)\left(x-4\right)$

$3x\left(11x^2y^2\right)$ $6x\left(3x^2-7x+8\right)$ $\left(2x+3\right)\left(3x-5\right)$

$9x^2\left(6x^2y^2\right)$ $7x\left(3x^2-4x+9\right)$ $\left(5x-6\right)\left(3x+4\right)$

5 Divide. **11 points**

$9x^4y^3\div 3xy^2$ $\left(9x+3\right)\div 3$ $\left(10x+8\right)\div 2$

$18x^3y^3\div 2x^2y^2$

$30x^4y^2\div 5x^2y^2$ $\left(12x-8\right)\div 4$ $\left(18x-12\right)\div 6$

$24x^5y^4\div 3x^2y^2$

$32x^5y^4\div 8x^2y^3$ $\left(15x-5\right)\div 5$ $\left(24x-9\right)\div 3$

57 points total

1 Multiply, using the FOIL method.

$(x+3)(x+5)$ $(x+8)(x-3)$

$(x+4)(x-6)$ $(2x+5)(x-4)$

$(2x-7)(x-4)$ $(2x+3)(3x-4)$

$(4x+3)(x-6)$ $(2x-5)(4x+3)$

2 Divide. **9 points**

$x+3\overline{)x^2+7x+12}$ $x-2\overline{)x^2+\ x-6}$ $x-4\overline{)2x^2-3x-20}$

$(x^2+6x+8)\div(x+2)$ $(2x^2-7x+6)\div(x-2)$ $(6x^2-5x-4)\div(3x-4)$

$(x^2-x-12)\div(x+3)$ $(3x^2-14x-5)\div(x-5)$ $(6x^2-17x-14)\div(2x-7)$

③ Graph.

Plot the given points in blue and join them to form a polygon. Graph the reflection over the *x*-axis in green and the reflection over the *y*-axis in red.

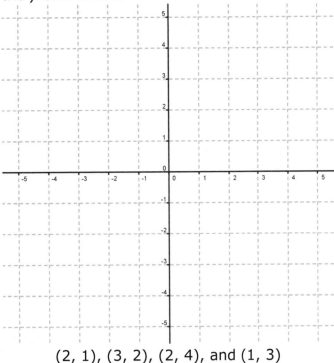

(2, 1), (3, 2), (2, 4), and (1, 3)

Plot the given points in blue and join them to form a polygon. Graph the translation down 4 units in green and the translation left 3 units in red.

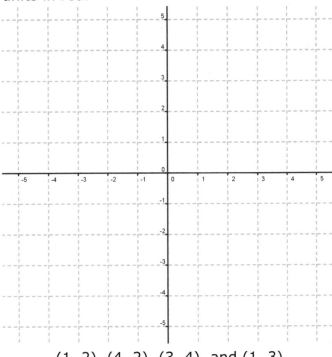

(1, 2), (4, 2), (3, 4), and (1, 3)

Plot the given points in blue and join them to form a polygon. Graph the rotation 90° clockwise in green and the rotation 90° counterclockwise in red.

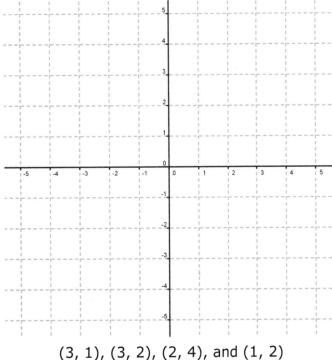

(3, 1), (3, 2), (2, 4), and (1, 2)

Plot the given points in blue and join them to form a polygon. Calculate the coordinates of the figure when you scale it by a factor of 0.5 and draw its graph in red. Calculate the coordinates of the figure when you scale it by a factor of 1.5 and draw its graph in green.

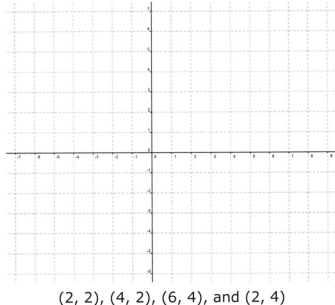

(2, 2), (4, 2), (6, 4), and (2, 4)

65 points total

1 Find the area of each shaded region. Label each answer with the proper units.   **18 points**

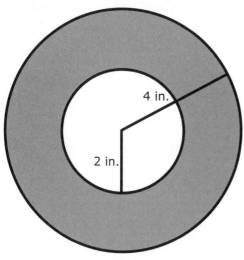

White circle:

Gray ring:

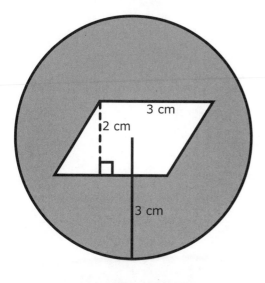

White parallelogram:

Gray region:

Multi-colored square:

A single black triangle:

A single gray triangle:

The entire gray region:

The entire black region:

In the square above, each pair of
adjacent acute angles is congruent and
complementary. Each pair of angles in
the center of each side is congruent and
supplementary. Each side of the square
is 12 feet long.

2 Find the perimeter and area of each regular polygon. Label each answer with the proper units.

12 points

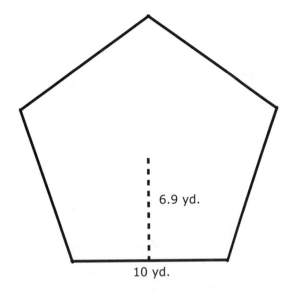

10 yd.

6.9 yd.

Perimeter:

Area:

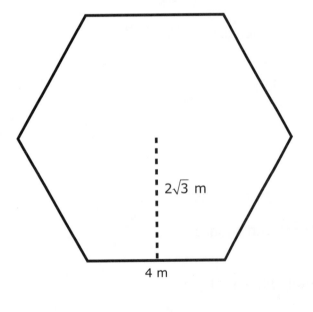

4 m

$2\sqrt{3}$ m

Perimeter:

Area:

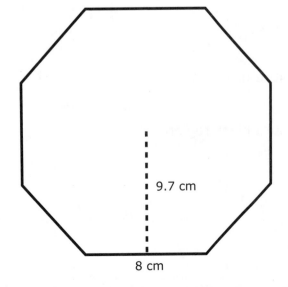

8 cm

9.7 cm

Perimeter:

Area:

30 points total

Horizons Pre-Algebra, Tests and Resources

1 Use the divisibility tests to tell if 2, 3, 4, 5, 6, and 9 are factors of each number. **24 points**

	114	115	116	117	118	120	123	124	126	135
2										
3										
4										
5										
6										
9										

2 Estimate the sum by rounding to the nearest thousand. **3 points**

$$\begin{aligned} 2809 \\ +1207 \end{aligned} \approx \qquad \begin{aligned} 4118 \\ +8978 \end{aligned} \approx \qquad \begin{aligned} 3987 \\ +4016 \end{aligned} \approx$$

3 Estimate each product by rounding to the nearest ten. **2 points**

$19 \times 132 \approx$ $\qquad\qquad$ $72 \times 28 \approx$

4 Solve, using the rules for signed numbers. **4 points**

$(+52) + (+23) =$ $\qquad\qquad$ $(-11)(5)(-2) =$

$(-11) + (+37) =$ $\qquad\qquad$ $(-6)(-9)(-1) =$

5 Solve, using the rules for absolute values. **4 points**

$|-8| + |-49| =$ $\qquad\qquad$ $|84| - |-16| =$

$|-13| + |92| =$ $\qquad\qquad$ $-|24| + |-6| =$

6 Solve. **4 points**

$$\begin{aligned} 82{,}194 \\ +12{,}917 \end{aligned} \qquad \begin{aligned} 61{,}591 \\ -31{,}467 \end{aligned} \qquad \begin{aligned} 248 \\ \times 76 \end{aligned} \qquad 53\overline{)1272}$$

7 Express the prime factorization of each number using exponents. **3 points**

$\qquad$ 81 $\qquad\qquad\qquad$ 84 $\qquad\qquad\qquad$ 100

8 Solve, following the order of operations. **2 points**

$3 \times \left(2^3 + 1\right) - 5 \times 3 =$

$3 \times 8 - \left(3^2 - 2^2 - 7\right) =$

9 Find the greatest common factor of each set of numbers.   **3 points**

12 and 15   16 and 24   9 and 12

10 Find the least common multiple of each set of numbers.   **3 points**

6 and 9   10 and 15   12 and 18

11 Simplify the roots.   **8 points**

$\sqrt{64} =$ $8\sqrt[3]{12} - 3\sqrt[3]{12} =$

$\sqrt{54} =$ $\left(\sqrt{5}\right)\left(3\sqrt{15}\right) =$

$\sqrt[3]{125} =$ $\sqrt{80} \div \sqrt{5} =$

$2\sqrt{19} + 5\sqrt{19} =$ $11 \div \sqrt{11} =$

12 Solve.   **3 points**

$5x + 13 - 4 = 44$ $x + 4 + 6 = 26 - 3x$ $3x + 4x - 16 + 11 = 23$

13 Solve the inequalities.   **3 points**

$4x - 3 < 13$ $3x + 11 > 5x - 17$ $3x + 8 < x - 14$

14 Solve.   **4 points**

682.4	819.3	76.3	
+49.74	−83.47	×8.9	$0.19\overline{)89.3}$

15 Solve.

$10^5 =$

$\left(10^2\right)\left(10^7\right) =$

$\left(10^{18}\right) \div \left(10^{11}\right) =$

$10^{-3} =$

$67.1 \times 10^2 =$

$0.038 \times 10^3 =$

$0.483 \times 10^{-1} =$

$69.15 \times 10^{-2} =$

$54.19 \div 10^0 =$

$3.45 \div 10^3 =$

$0.32 \div 10^{-1} =$

$0.04 \div 10^{-2} =$

16 Write an equation and solve.

2 points

At Billy's concession stand, a cheeseburger with potato chips costs 4 times as much as a candy-filled sucker and 2 pieces of bubble gum. If a candy-filled sucker costs 25 cents and bubble gum costs 5 cents each, how much does Billy charge for a cheeseburger with potato chips?

17 Multiply or divide the appropriate powers of 10 to complete the metric conversions.   **8 points**

0.3 km = _____ m

6.7 kL = _____ L

1794 L = _____ kL

32.8 W = _____ kW

0.25 m = _____ mm

6.5 L = _____ cL

6791 mL = _____ L

826 cm = _____ m

18 Solve the numerators to make equivalent fractions.   **4 points**

$\dfrac{3}{8} = \dfrac{}{24}$ $\dfrac{2}{5} = \dfrac{}{20}$ $\dfrac{9}{10} = \dfrac{}{90}$ $\dfrac{5}{6} = \dfrac{}{24}$

19 Complete the fraction-decimal equivalents.   **8 points**

$\dfrac{1}{2} =$ $\dfrac{1}{6} =$ $\dfrac{3}{4} =$ $\dfrac{2}{5} =$

$0.25 =$ $0.\overline{6} =$ $0.625 =$ $0.4 =$

20 Add, subtract, multiply, or divide as indicated.   **4 points**

$\dfrac{2}{3} + \dfrac{1}{4} =$

$\dfrac{4}{5} \times \dfrac{15}{16} =$

$\dfrac{7}{10} - \dfrac{2}{3} =$

$\dfrac{3}{5} \div \dfrac{7}{10} =$

108 points total

1 Use the divisibility tests to tell if 2, 3, 4, 5, 6, and 9 are factors of each number. **12 points**

	2	3	4	5	6	9
172						
174						
175						
180						

2 Express the prime factorization of each number using exponents. **3 points**

76   99   125

3 Solve, following the order of operations. **2 points**

$$\sqrt{2 \times (3^3 - 2) - 1} =$$

$$4 \times 5 - \sqrt{3^2 + 2^3 - 1} =$$

4 Solve. **3 points**

$7x + 15 - 6 = 44$ $\dfrac{3x}{2} + 4 + 7 = 26$ $3x + 4(x - 1) + 11 < 24$

5 Add, subtract, multiply, or divide as indicated. **4 points**

$1\dfrac{2}{3} + 2\dfrac{1}{4} =$

$3\dfrac{7}{10} - 1\dfrac{2}{3} =$

$1\dfrac{2}{3} \times 2\dfrac{1}{10} =$

$2\dfrac{1}{5} \div 1\dfrac{1}{10} =$

6 Write each number in scientific notation. **4 points**

490,000,000   0.000000218

34,000,000   0.00043

7 Solve.

What is 65% of 80?   42 is 70% of what number?   35 is what percent of 140?

8 Complete the chart to reflect simple interest.   **6 points**

Principal	Interest rate	Time in years	Amount of interest	Total amount paid
$1000	5%	4		
$5000	7%	6		
$10,000	9%	8		

9 Calculate the equivalent length for each given length.   **8 points**

7 miles	yards
8 miles	feet
11 yards	inches
51 feet	yards
15 inches	cm
8 inches	mm
9 yards	meters
7 miles	km

10 Use the formula $A = P(1+r)^t$ to calculate compound interest.   **6 points**

Initial principal	Interest rate	Time in years	Total compounded annually	Total compounded quarterly
$1000	5%	4		
$5000	7%	6		
$10,000	9%	8		

Horizons Pre-Algebra, Tests and Resources

11 Find the mean, median, and mode.

3 points

The results of 20 rolls of a die are 2, 5, 6, 2, 3, 1, 2, 6, 1, 1, 5, 2, 3, 1, 5, 6, 2, 4, 4, 2. Round answers to the nearest tenth where appropriate.

12 Make a stem-and-leaf plot and find the range.

11 points

The points scored by the top 25 NCAA men's basketball teams are as follows: 85, 81, 90, 59, 57, 95, 70, 77, 77, 82, 89, 60, 79, 76, 77, 57, 63, 75, 68, 84, 69, 98, 85, 65, 55.

13 Draw a histogram, list the 5-number summary, and draw a box-and-whisker plot.

7 points

The points scored by the top 25 NCAA men's basketball teams are as follows: 85, 81, 90, 59, 57, 95, 70, 77, 77, 82, 89, 60, 79, 76, 77, 57, 63, 75, 68, 84, 69, 98, 85, 65, 55.

14 Complete the chart to show probability and odds.

Scenario	Number of Possible Outcomes	Desired Event (E)	P(E)	Odds (in Favor of E)	Odds (Against E)
Flip a coin once		Tails			
Roll a 6-sided die once		Even number			
Choose an integer from 1 to 10		Prime number			

15 Calculate the permutations and combinations. **8 points**

$p(8,2) =$ $C(8,2) =$

$p(5,3) =$ $C(5,3) =$

$p(6,4) =$ $C(6,4) =$

$p(8,3) =$ $C(8,3) =$

16 Solve. **4 points**

A card game has 4 different colors of cards and 13 different numbers on the cards. How many combinations are possible with one color and one number?

A school has 3 different choices for shirts, 4 different choices for pants, and 3 different choices for sweaters for the school uniform. How many different uniform combinations are possible?

You roll 5 dice at one time. What is the probability that you will roll a 2 on all 5 dice?

If you rolled a 3 on 3 of the dice on your first roll, what is the probability that you will roll a 3 with your two remaining dice on your second roll?

96 points total

1 Find the probabilities.

When a standard six-sided game die is rolled one time, what is the probability that it will be a 1 or a 6?

When a standard six-sided game die is rolled twice, what is the probability that the first roll will be a 1 and the second roll will be a 6?

When a standard six-sided game die is rolled twice, what is the probability that a 1 and a 6 will be rolled in either order?

2 Find the lateral area, surface area, and volume of each solid figure.   **14 points**

A prism with a height of 8 feet and a rectangular base that is 7 feet long and 4 feet wide.

A pyramid with a height of 12 meters, a slant height of 13 meters, and a square base that is 10 meters on each side.

A cylinder with a height of 7 inches and a base that has a diameter of 4 inches.

A cone with a height of 8 yards, a slant height of 10 yards, and a base that has a diameter of 12 yards.

A sphere with a diameter of 18 cm.

Exam 3

3 points

3 Use the formula $m = \frac{w}{g}$ to find the mass or weight of each item. Round answers to the nearest whole number. **3 points**

	Baby	Child	Adult
Mass		32.1 kg	
Weight	40 kg • m/s²		800 kg • m/s²
Gravity	9.8 m/s²	9.8 m/s²	9.8 m/s²

4 Use the formula $d = \frac{m}{v}$ to find the density of each object and identify if it will float in pure water. The density of pure water is 1000 kg/m³. **6 points**

Substance	Mass	Volume	Density	Float: Y/N
Cocoa beans	237.2 kg	0.4 m³		
Brick	2325.62 kg	1.21 m³		
Furnace cinders	2282.5 kg	2.5 m³		

5 Use the formula $v = \frac{d}{t}$ to find the velocity, distance, or time. **3 points**

Velocity	Distance	Time
	585 miles	9 hours
48 miles per hour		1.5 hours
340 miles per hour	884 miles	

6 Identify one of each item in circle *A*. Write the appropriate symbol for each figure. **6 points**

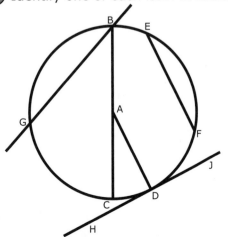

Secant   Chord

Diameter   Tangent

Radius   Central angle

Horizons Pre-Algebra, Tests and Resources

7 Graph the following equations on your own graph paper.   **3 points**

$y = x - 3$

$y = -4x + 1$

$y \geq 2(x + 1)$

8 Write each equation in slope-intercept form and identify the slope and *y*-intercept.   **18 points**

$-4x + y - 5 = 0$

$-3x + y + 7 = 0$

$10x + y - 13 = 0$

$4x + 2y + 7 = 0$

$6x + 2y + 9 = 0$

$7x + 2y - 5 = 0$

9 Solve. Express the answer as a coordinate point.   **6 points**

$2x + 2y + 1 = 0$
$2x + y - 1 = 0$

$4x - 2y + 4 = 0$
$-4x + 3y - 3 = 0$

$3x + y + 5 = 0$
$-2x - y + 1 = 0$

10 Find the measure of each angle in the figure below.   **13 points**

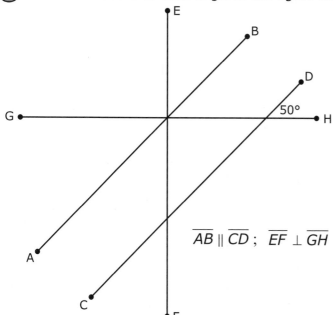

$\overline{AB} \parallel \overline{CD} \,; \;\; \overline{EF} \perp \overline{GH}$

75 points total

Horizons Pre-Algebra, Tests and Resources

1 Complete the chart to show temperature conversions.   **6 points**

°F	°C		°C	°F
59°			25°	
77°			35°	
23°			45°	

2 Solve.   **3 points**

Convert 28 ounces to milliliters.

Convert 10 quarts to liters.

Convert 35 gallons to liters.

3 Find the lengths of the missing sides. Then find the sine, cosine, and tangent of each acute angle.   **8 points**

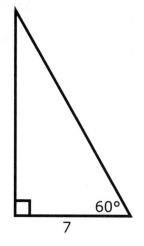

$\sin 30° =$

$\cos 30° =$

$\tan 30° =$

$\sin 60° =$

$\cos 60° =$

$\tan 60° =$

4 Add or subtract.   **6 points**

$$3x^2 + 5x + 8$$
$$+\ 4x^2 + 3x + 6$$

$$2x^2 + 8x + 7$$
$$+x^2 - 6x - 9$$

$$5x^2 - 3x + 9$$
$$+4x^2 + 2x - 7$$

$$\left(4x^2 + 5x + 8\right)$$
$$-\left(3x^2 + 3x + 6\right)$$

$$\left(4x^2 - 8x + 9\right)$$
$$-\left(2x^2 - 6x - 7\right)$$

$$\left(5x^2 - 2x - 7\right)$$
$$-\left(2x^2 + 3x - 9\right)$$

5 Multiply or divide.   **6 points**

$3x\left(8xy^2\right)$

$7x\left(3x^2 + 3x - 2\right)$

$5x\left(3x^2 - 7x + 8\right)$

$18x^4y^3 \div 3xy^2$

$\left(24x - 8\right) \div 4$

$\left(12x + 9\right) \div 3$

6 Multiply, using the FOIL method.

$(x+2)(x+7)$ $(x+4)(x-5)$

7 Divide.

$x+2\overline{)x^2+9x+14}$ $x-4\overline{)x^2+2x-24}$ $x-5\overline{)2x^2-7x-15}$

8 Graph.

Plot the given points in blue and join them to form a polygon. Graph the reflection over the x-axis in green and the reflection over the y-axis in red.

Plot the given points in blue and join them to form a polygon. Graph the translation down 4 units in green and the translation left 3 units in red.

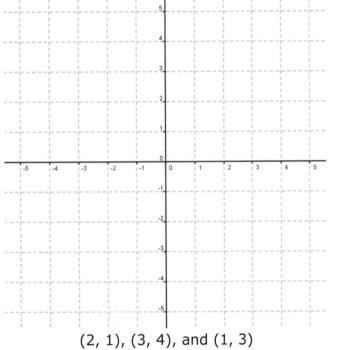

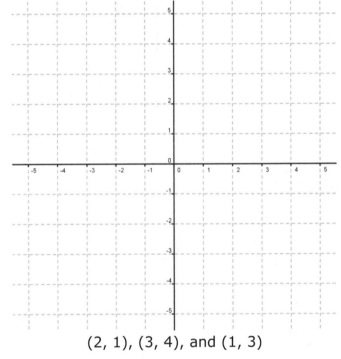

(2, 1), (3, 4), and (1, 3)   (2, 1), (3, 4), and (1, 3)

9 Find the area of each region. Label each answer with the proper units.

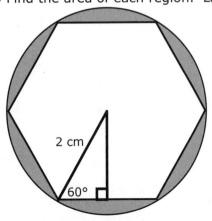

2 cm

60°

White regular hexagon:

Gray shaded area:

10 Express the prime factorization of each number using exponents.   **3 points**

81   99   125

11 Solve.   **3 points**

$8x + 15 - 4 = 59$

$\dfrac{3x}{2} + 4 + 7 = 26$

$x + 2(x - 2) + 11 < 46$

12 Add, subtract, multiply, or divide as indicated.   **4 points**

$1\dfrac{2}{3} + 2\dfrac{1}{4} =$

$3\dfrac{7}{10} - 1\dfrac{2}{3} =$

$1\dfrac{2}{3} \times 2\dfrac{1}{10} =$

$2\dfrac{1}{5} \div 1\dfrac{1}{10} =$

13 Solve.   **3 points**

What is 65% of 80?   42 is 70% of what number?   35 is what percent of 140?

14 Complete the chart to reflect simple interest.   **6 points**

Principal	Interest rate	Time in years	Amount of interest	Total amount paid
$1,500	5%	4		
$5,000	7%	6		
$10,000	9%	8		

15 Calculate the equivalent length for each given length. **6 points**

6 miles	yards
8 miles	feet
13 yards	inches
8 inches	mm
11 yards	meters
7 miles	km

16 Use the formula $A = P(1+r)^t$ to calculate compound interest. **4 points**

Initial principal	Interest rate	Time in years	Total compounded annually	Total compounded quarterly
$5,000	7%	6		
$10,000	9%	8		

17 Find the mean, median, and mode. **3 points**

The results of 20 rolls of a die are 2, 5, 6, 2, 3, 1, 2, 6, 1, 1, 5, 2, 3, 1, 5, 6, 2, 4, 4, 2. Round answers to the nearest tenth where appropriate.

18 Complete the chart to show probability and odds. **8 points**

Scenario	Number of Possible Outcomes	Desired Event (E)	P(E)	Odds (in Favor of E)	Odds (Against E)
Flip a coin once		Heads			
Roll a 6-sided die once		Odd number			

19 Calculate the permutations and combinations. **8 points**

p(6,4) =   C(8,2) =

p(8,3) =   C(5,3) =

20 Find the lateral area, surface area, and volume of each solid figure.   **8 points**

A prism with a height of 6 feet and a rectangular base that is 9 feet long and 3 feet wide.

A cone with a height of 8 yards, a slant height of 10 yards, and a base that has a diameter of 12 yards.

A sphere with a diameter of 20 cm.

21 Identify one of each item in circle *A*. Write the appropriate symbol for each figure.   **6 points**

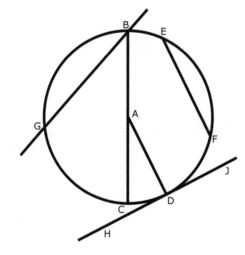

Secant

Diameter

Radius

Chord

Tangent

Central angle

22 Graph the following equations on your own graph paper.   **3 points**

$y = x - 2$ $y = -2x + 1$ $y \geq 2(x - 1)$

23 Write each equation in slope-intercept form and identify the slope and y-intercept.   **9 points**

$-3x + y - 4 = 0$ $-5x + y + 3 = 0$ $12x + y - 17 = 0$

24 Solve. Express the answer as a coordinate point.   **6 points**

$2x + 2y + 3 = 0$ $3x - 2y + 4 = 0$ $3x + y + 5 = 0$
$2x + \ y - 3 = 0$ $-3x + 3y - 3 = 0$ $-2x - y + 1 = 0$

25 Find the measure of each angle in the figure below.   **12 points**

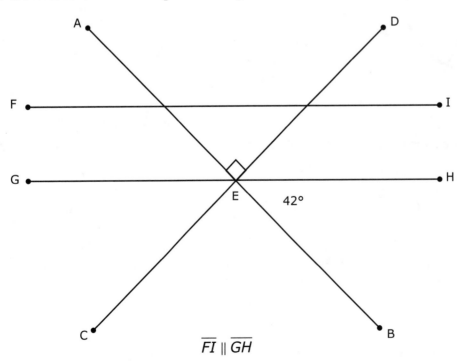

$\overline{FI} \parallel \overline{GH}$

148 points total

Horizons Pre-Algebra, Tests and Resources

5-digit Addition and Subtraction

1 Add.

$$
\begin{array}{r} 1454 \\ +8036 \\ \hline \end{array}
\qquad
\begin{array}{r} 7213 \\ +3885 \\ \hline \end{array}
\qquad
\begin{array}{r} 8353 \\ +7667 \\ \hline \end{array}
\qquad
\begin{array}{r} 2492 \\ +4698 \\ \hline \end{array}
$$

$$
\begin{array}{r} 34268 \\ +21327 \\ \hline \end{array}
\qquad
\begin{array}{r} 68096 \\ +41483 \\ \hline \end{array}
\qquad
\begin{array}{r} 65345 \\ +34572 \\ \hline \end{array}
\qquad
\begin{array}{r} 24888 \\ +24587 \\ \hline \end{array}
$$

$$
\begin{array}{r} 353110 \\ +128277 \\ \hline \end{array}
\qquad
\begin{array}{r} 949269 \\ +654698 \\ \hline \end{array}
\qquad
\begin{array}{r} 319269 \\ +847185 \\ \hline \end{array}
\qquad
\begin{array}{r} 136653 \\ +345702 \\ \hline \end{array}
$$

2 Subtract.

$$
\begin{array}{r} 3357 \\ -1738 \\ \hline \end{array}
\qquad
\begin{array}{r} 9940 \\ -2116 \\ \hline \end{array}
\qquad
\begin{array}{r} 7897 \\ -6268 \\ \hline \end{array}
\qquad
\begin{array}{r} 8023 \\ -6651 \\ \hline \end{array}
$$

$$
\begin{array}{r} 41940 \\ -22782 \\ \hline \end{array}
\qquad
\begin{array}{r} 81242 \\ -74580 \\ \hline \end{array}
\qquad
\begin{array}{r} 91661 \\ -36877 \\ \hline \end{array}
\qquad
\begin{array}{r} 77985 \\ -75573 \\ \hline \end{array}
$$

$$
\begin{array}{r} 520852 \\ -497823 \\ \hline \end{array}
\qquad
\begin{array}{r} 507669 \\ -304727 \\ \hline \end{array}
\qquad
\begin{array}{r} 452478 \\ -251972 \\ \hline \end{array}
\qquad
\begin{array}{r} 702928 \\ -653841 \\ \hline \end{array}
$$

2-digit Multiplication, 3-digit by 2-digit Division

1 Multiply.

46	23	55	32
×32	×65	×41	×68

238	415	714	465
×32	×93	×22	×39

808	753	379	835
×893	×627	×759	×146

2 Divide.

$16\overline{)144}$ $18\overline{)144}$ $17\overline{)153}$ $19\overline{)133}$

$13\overline{)195}$ $14\overline{)406}$ $16\overline{)272}$ $19\overline{)342}$

$16\overline{)592}$ $24\overline{)456}$ $23\overline{)575}$ $27\overline{)756}$

Identify Numbers, Estimate Sums and Products

1 Identify each number as *natural*, *whole*, *integer*, *rational*, *irrational*, or *real*.
Some numbers may have more than one answer.

	$3\sqrt{7}$	-8	π	0	$3\frac{2}{5}$	$\frac{9}{8}$	21	$\frac{1}{3}$	37.1
Natural									
Whole									
Integer									
Rational									
Irrational									
Real									

2 Estimate the sum by rounding to the nearest hundred.

$205 \atop +197$ $\approx$ $494 \atop +303$ $\approx$ $406 \atop +296$ $\approx$ $688 \atop +213$ $\approx$

$318 \atop +774$ $\approx$ $328 \atop +981$ $\approx$ $886 \atop +219$ $\approx$ $301 \atop +597$ $\approx$

3 Estimate each product by rounding to the nearest ten.

12 x 127 $\approx$

88 x 21 $\approx$

49 x 71 $\approx$

51 x 69 $\approx$

28 x 32 $\approx$

99 x 252 $\approx$

77 x 82 $\approx$

32 x 47 $\approx$

Horizons Pre-Algebra, Tests and Resources

Signed Numbers, Absolute Value

1 Solve, using the rules for signed numbers.

(+8) + (+5) =

(-8) + (+5) =

(-8) + (-5) =

(+8) + (-5) =

(+8) − (-5) =

(-8) − (-5) =

(8)(5) =

(8)(-5) =

(-8)(5) =

(-8)(-5) =

2 Solve, using the rules of absolute values.

$|14| =$

$|-31| =$

$-|27| =$

$-|29| =$

$-|-18| =$

$|26 + 10| =$

$-|22 + 11| =$

$|-2 + 15| =$

Factors and Multiples

1 Find all of the factors for each of the following numbers and identify as prime or composite.

11 _____   _____

12 _____   _____

13 _____   _____

14 _____   _____

15 _____   _____

16 _____   _____

17 _____   _____

18 _____   _____

19 _____   _____

20 _____   _____

2 Write 5 multiples of each of the following numbers.

5 _____

6 _____

7 _____

8 _____

9 _____

11 _____

12 _____

13 _____

15 _____

3 Find the prime factorization of each of the following numbers.

| 12 | 25 | 32 |

Exponential Form

1 Write the expanded form expressions in exponential form. Do not solve them.

$2 \times 2 \times 2 \times 2 \times 2 =$

$8 \times 8 \times 8 =$

$11 \times 11 \times 11 \times 11 \times 11 \times 11 \times 11 \times 11 =$

$5 \times 5 \times 5 \times 5 \times 5 \times 5 =$

$14 \times 14 \times 14 \times 14 =$

2 Write the following exponential expressions in expanded form and solve.

$4^2 =$

$7^2 =$

$3^3 =$

$10^2 =$

$2^4 =$

3 Find the prime factorization of each number. Use exponents where appropriate.

| 18 | 24 | 27 |

Squares, Order of Operations

1 Find the square of each number.

2	6
3	7
4	8
5	9

2 Simplify each expression, following the proper order of operations.

$6 + 12 \div 3 =$

$27 - 5 \times 2 =$

$16 - 3 \times 4 + 9 =$

$4 + 8 \times 5 \div 4 =$

$15 \div 3 \times 6 + 4 - 2 \times 2 =$

$16 \div (2 \times 4) + 5 - 1 \times 3 =$

$(11 - 3) \times 3 - 16 =$

$(11 - 6)^2 - 18 \div 3 =$

$(11 + 6) - 3^2 + 2 \times 4 =$

$(8 - 5)^3 - 4^2 - 3 \times 2 =$

$2^3 \times 4 \div (9 + 7) - 3 =$

$(6^2 - (12 + 13) + 7) \div 3 =$

$((8 + 4 \times 3) \div 5)^2 =$

Order of Operations

1 Simplify each expression, following the proper order of operations.

$13 + 18 \div 9 =$

$36 - 4 \times 6 =$

$37 - 4 \times 7 - 5 =$

$6 + 9 \times 8 \div 12 =$

$33 \div 3 \times 4 + 4 - 2 \times 7 =$

$36 \div (3 \times 6) + 9 - 2 \times 4 =$

$(25 - 20) \times 4 - 19 =$

$(12 - 3)^2 - 20 \times 3 =$

$(13 + 8) - 4^2 + 3 \times 2 =$

$(9 - 7)^3 + 3^2 - 4 \times 2 =$

$3^3 \div 9 \times (11 - 7) - 6 =$

$(8^2 - (15 + 19) + 9) \div 13 =$

$((4 + 3 \times 7) \div 5)^2 =$

$(9 + 18 \div 3 - 5)^2 \div 2 + 13 =$

$1^3 + 2^3 - 3^2 \times 4^0 + 9 \div 3 =$

Exponents, Divisibility Tests, GCF

1 Simplify the expressions. You do not have to solve exponents greater than 3.

$7^0 =$ $2^{-3} =$

$16^1 =$

$5^2 \times 5^6 =$ $\left(\dfrac{1}{5}\right)^2 =$

$7^9 \div 7^7 =$

$\left(2 \times 3\right)^2 =$ $\left(\dfrac{2}{3}\right)^{-2} =$

2 Use the divisibility tests to determine which numbers are factors of the given numbers.

	2	3	4	5	6	9	10
471							
492							
459							
540							
612							
606							
453							

3 Find the greatest common factor of each set of numbers.

9 and 15   16 and 20   6, 9, and 15

Horizons Pre-Algebra, Tests and Resources

LCM, GCF, Radical Expressions

1 Find the greatest common factor of each set of numbers.

12 and 16   16 and 18   18 and 24

15 and 24   20 and 24   12, 15, and 18

2 Find the least common multiple of each set of numbers.

4 and 6   9 and 15   12 and 16

8 and 10   12 and 15   14 and 24

3 Rewrite the following expressions as roots.

$3^5 = 243$ $8^3 = 512$

$9^2 = 81$ $10^4 = 10,000$

$4^3 = 64$ $5^2 = 25$

Radicals, Writing Mathematical Expressions

1 Rewrite the following expressions as roots.

$4^5 = 1024$

$13^2 = 169$

$8^2 = 64$

$3^4 = 81$

$5^3 = 125$

$11^2 = 121$

2 Solve the following roots.

$\sqrt{16} =$

$\sqrt[3]{64} =$

$\sqrt{36} =$

$6\sqrt{11} + 2\sqrt{11} =$

$\sqrt{12} =$

$\sqrt{15} + 4\sqrt{15} =$

$\sqrt{18} =$

$\sqrt{32} =$

$16\sqrt{7} - 9\sqrt{7} =$

$\sqrt{44} =$

$\left(\sqrt{2}\right)\left(\sqrt{5}\right) =$

$\sqrt[3]{8} =$

$\left(2\sqrt{18}\right)\left(3\sqrt{8}\right) =$

$\sqrt[3]{27} =$

$\sqrt[3]{40} \div \sqrt[3]{5} =$

$\sqrt[3]{40} =$

$\sqrt[3]{54} =$

$15\sqrt{12} \div 3\sqrt{6} =$

$\sqrt[3]{16} =$

$\sqrt{50} \div 5 =$

3 Translate the following words into a mathematical expression.

The total of a number and 17 _____

6 fewer than a number _____

A number times 9 _____

The sum of 35 and a number _____

The quotient of a number and 8 _____

13 less than a number _____

A number increased by a factor of 4 _____

61 more than a number _____

A number less than 72 _____

The product of 9 and a number _____

The ratio of a number to 3 _____

A number increased by 46 _____

Addition and Subtraction of Decimals

1 Add.

1454.18	7213.491	8353.5	2492.95
+8036.37	+3885.653	+7667.1	+4698.42

3426.8	680.96	65.345	248.88
+ 213.27	+4148.3	+3457.2	+ 2.4587

35.311	9492.69	31926.9	136.653
+1282.77	+65469.8	+ 84.7185	+ 37.5702

2 Subtract.

3357.679	9940.08	7897.4	8023.587
−1738.154	−2116.35	−6268.9	−6651.45

41940.267	81242.54	91661.7	7798.5
−22782.49	−74580.054	−36877.648	− 75.573

52085.2	507.669	452.478	7.02928
− 49.7823	− 30.4727	−251.9	−0.653841

Combining Like Terms

① Simplify by combining like terms.

$x + 6 + 2 =$

$x + 8 + 14 =$

$x + x + 9 + 2 =$

$x + x + 12 + 11 =$

$2x + x + 18 - 12 =$

$2x + 5x + 17 - 15 =$

$3x + 4x - 7 + 4 =$

$7x + 2x + 18 - 7 =$

$9x - 4x + 24 - 15 - 7 =$

$7x - 5x + 15 - 8 - 4 =$

$5x + 9x - 4x - 8 - 6 + 12 =$

$10x + 2x - 7x - 10 - 8 + 13 =$

② Solve by combining like terms.

$x + 12 = 23$

$2x - 7 = 19$

$x + 6 + 7 = 22$

$x + x + 3 + 11 = 30$

$2x + x + 9 - 5 = 22$

$3x + 2x - 18 + 13 = 35$

$4x - 2x + 15 - 10 - 6 = 19$

$4x + 3x - x - 8 - 6 + 4 = 32$

$5x + 6 = 4x + 11$

$x + 16 \div 4 = 4x + 1$

$3(x - 2) = 2x + 5$

$2(x - 3) = 3(x + 3)$

Solving Inequalities, Operations with Decimals

1 Solve the inequalities.

$4x < 20$ $\qquad$ $6x + 7 > 25$ $\qquad$ $5x - 3 < 2x + 9$

$-4x < 20$ $\qquad$ $3x + 4 > x - 4$ $\qquad$ $6x + 7 < 8x + 5$

2 Solve.

67.91	51.3	475.96	429.15	430.7
+43.65	+64.27	+ 23.81	+743.3	+ 26.81

39.749	243.74	695.2	189.72	768.2
−16.237	− 65.19	− 47.23	− 99.999	− 92.4537

9.2	6.5	85.1	8.42	.473
× 7	× .3	× .9	× 7.3	× .19

$.6\overline{)2.4}$ $\qquad$ $.4\overline{).28}$ $\qquad$ $.5\overline{)35}$ $\qquad$ $9\overline{)4.5}$

Powers of Ten

1 Solve.

$10^5 =$

$10^6 =$

$10^{-5} =$

$10^{-7} =$

2 Simplify.

$(10^4)(10^7) =$

$(10^{14}) \div (10^8) =$

$(10^8)(10^{-5}) =$

$(10^3) \div (10^{-1}) =$

3 Simplify.

$9 \times 10^0 =$

$.7 \times 10^1 =$

$.35 \times 10^2 =$

$8.14 \times 10^3 =$

$4.83 \times 10^0 =$

$.571 \times 10^1 =$

$46.3 \times 10^2 =$

$.076 \times 10^3 =$

$19 \times 10^0 =$

$13 \times 10^{-1} =$

$27 \times 10^{-2} =$

$39 \times 10^{-3} =$

$3.28 \div 10^0 =$

$7.48 \div 10^1 =$

$26.91 \div 10^2 =$

$44.58 \div 10^3 =$

$0.561 \div 10^0 =$

$0.97 \div 10^1 =$

$0.36 \div 10^2 =$

$0.4 \div 10^3 =$

Operations with Powers of Ten

1 Solve.

$10^5 =$ $10^{-5} =$

$10^8 =$ $10^{-2} =$

$(10^2)(10^7) =$ $(10^{10})(10^{-4}) =$

$(10^{15}) \div (10^9) =$ $(10^5) \div (10^{-2}) =$

2 Multiply.

$12 \times 10^0 =$ $0.15 \times 10^0 =$

$0.7 \times 10^1 =$ $0.5796 \times 10^1 =$

$0.63 \times 10^2 =$ $45.27 \times 10^2 =$

$4.29 \times 10^3 =$ $0.072 \times 10^3 =$

$54.29 \times 10^0 =$ $47.34 \times 10^0 =$

$0.748 \times 10^1 =$ $0.982 \times 10^1 =$

$8.19 \times 10^2 =$ $5.194 \times 10^2 =$

$0.026 \times 10^3 =$ $0.008 \times 10^3 =$

3 Multiply or divide as indicated.

$16 \times 10^0 =$ $6.4 \times 10^0 =$

$8 \times 10^{-1} =$ $38 \times 10^{-1} =$

$4 \times 10^{-2} =$ $67 \times 10^{-2} =$

$17 \times 10^{-3} =$ $9.4 \times 10^{-3} =$

$8.34 \div 10^0 =$ $0.182 \div 10^0 =$

$6.95 \div 10^1 =$ $0.493 \div 10^1 =$

$5.49 \div 10^2 =$ $0.047 \div 10^2 =$

$47.13 \div 10^3 =$ $0.7 \div 10^3 =$

Decimal—Fraction Conversions

1 Convert the fractions to decimals.

$\dfrac{3}{20} =$ $\dfrac{5}{16} =$

$\dfrac{7}{50} =$ $\dfrac{7}{9} =$

$\dfrac{9}{25} =$ $\dfrac{13}{20} =$

$\dfrac{4}{15} =$ $\dfrac{37}{50} =$

$\dfrac{1}{9} =$ $\dfrac{11}{30} =$

$\dfrac{9}{40} =$ $\dfrac{19}{40} =$

2 Convert the decimals to fractions. Reduce all fractions to lowest terms.

0.18   0.018

0.36   0.036

0.49   0.049

0.66   0.066

0.24   0.024

0.55   0.055

Metric Conversions

1 Multiply or divide the appropriate powers of 10 to complete the metric conversions.

54 kg = _____ g   43 g = _____ cg

0.13 km = _____ m   0.87 m = _____ mm

5.8 kL = _____ L   3.7 L = _____ cL

32.49 kW = _____ W   54.91 W = _____ mW

17,000 g = _____ kg   3000 cg = _____ g

4971 L = _____ kL   1943 mL = _____ L

394 m = _____ km   325 cm = _____ m

45.7 W = _____ kW   39.5 mW = _____ W

2 kg = _____ g   10 g = _____ cg

0.5 km = _____ m   0.4 m = _____ mm

0.8 kL = _____ L   1.2 L = _____ cL

72.18 kW = _____ W   2.49 W = _____ mW

6481 g = _____ kg   5614 cg = _____ g

9157 L = _____ kL   914 mL = _____ L

329 m = _____ km   83 cm = _____ m

17.4 W = _____ kW   95.43 mW = _____ W

0.8 kg = _____ g   1 g = _____ cg

0.17 km = _____ m   1 m = _____ mm

13.8 kL = _____ L   6.7 L = _____ cL

62.4 kW = _____ W   1.817 W = _____ mW

9080 g = _____ kg   43 cg = _____ g

716.8 L = _____ kL   90,483 mL = _____ L

319 m = _____ km   5 cm = _____ m

Decimal to Fraction Equivalents

1 Complete the fraction-decimal equivalents.

$\dfrac{1}{2} =$ $0.1 =$

$\dfrac{1}{3} =$ $0.125 =$

$\dfrac{1}{4} =$ $0.1\overline{6} =$

$\dfrac{1}{5} =$ $0.2 =$

$\dfrac{1}{6} =$ $0.25 =$

$\dfrac{1}{8} =$ $0.3 =$

$\dfrac{1}{10} =$ $0.\overline{3} =$

$\dfrac{2}{3} =$ $0.375 =$

$\dfrac{2}{5} =$ $0.4 =$

$\dfrac{3}{4} =$ $0.5 =$

$\dfrac{3}{5} =$ $0.6 =$

$\dfrac{3}{8} =$ $0.625 =$

$\dfrac{3}{10} =$ $0.\overline{6} =$

$\dfrac{4}{5} =$ $0.7 =$

$\dfrac{5}{6} =$ $0.75 =$

$\dfrac{5}{8} =$ $0.8 =$

$\dfrac{7}{8} =$ $0.8\overline{3} =$

$\dfrac{7}{10} =$ $0.875 =$

$\dfrac{9}{10} =$ $0.9 =$

English to Metric Conversions

1 Complete the chart to show correct English length equivalents.

12 miles	yards
12 miles	feet
6 yards	inches
132 feet	yards
15 yards	feet
36,960 feet	miles
19,360 yards	miles
14 feet	inches
192 inches	feet
504 inches	yards
8 miles	feet
9 yards	inches
96 feet	yards

2 Complete the chart to show correct English-Metric conversions.

19 inches	cm
14 inches	mm
11 yards	meters
9 miles	km
32 cm	inches
8 meters	yards
13 km	miles
20 inches	cm
8 inches	mm
15 yards	meters
18 miles	km
17 cm	inches
11 meters	yards
10 km	miles

Addition of Mixed Numbers

1 Add.

$2\dfrac{3}{7} + 3\dfrac{1}{7} =$

$3\dfrac{1}{3} + 2\dfrac{1}{3} =$

$2\dfrac{2}{7} + 5\dfrac{4}{7} =$

$2\dfrac{3}{8} + 3\dfrac{1}{4} =$

$1\dfrac{3}{5} + 6\dfrac{3}{10} =$

$2\dfrac{2}{3} + 5\dfrac{3}{4} =$

2 Add, using the alternative method.

$2\dfrac{3}{7} + 3\dfrac{1}{7} =$

$3\dfrac{1}{3} + 2\dfrac{1}{3} =$

$2\dfrac{2}{7} + 5\dfrac{4}{7} =$

$2\dfrac{3}{8} + 3\dfrac{1}{4} =$

$1\dfrac{3}{5} + 6\dfrac{3}{10} =$

$2\dfrac{2}{3} + 5\dfrac{3}{4} =$

Horizons Pre-Algebra, Tests and Resources   99

Subtraction of Mixed Numbers

1 Subtract.

$8\dfrac{5}{8} - 5\dfrac{1}{8} =$

$5\dfrac{3}{4} - 1\dfrac{1}{2} =$

$7\dfrac{2}{3} - 3\dfrac{1}{6} =$

$5\dfrac{3}{10} - 2\dfrac{1}{5} =$

$3\dfrac{1}{4} - 1\dfrac{7}{8} =$

$8\dfrac{1}{4} - 5\dfrac{2}{3} =$

2 Subtract, using the alternate method.

$8\dfrac{5}{8} - 5\dfrac{1}{8} =$

$5\dfrac{3}{4} - 1\dfrac{1}{2} =$

$7\dfrac{2}{3} - 3\dfrac{1}{6} =$

$5\dfrac{3}{10} - 2\dfrac{1}{5} =$

$3\dfrac{1}{4} - 1\dfrac{7}{8} =$

$8\dfrac{1}{4} - 5\dfrac{2}{3} =$

English to Metric Length Conversion

1 Complete the chart to show correct English length equivalents.

7 miles	yards
4 yards	inches
102 feet	yards
31,680 feet	miles
15,840 yards	miles
360 inches	yards
4 miles	feet

2 Complete the chart to show correct English-Metric conversions.

11 inches	cm
13 inches	mm
12 yards	meters
6 miles	km
20 cm	inches
7 meters	yards
5 km	miles

Proportions

1 Write = or ≠ to indicate if each pair of ratios forms a proportion.

$\dfrac{12}{75}$ $\dfrac{16}{100}$ $\dfrac{15}{25}$ $\dfrac{25}{35}$

$\dfrac{4}{5}$ $\dfrac{16}{25}$ $\dfrac{64}{24}$ $\dfrac{24}{9}$

$\dfrac{10}{15}$ $\dfrac{25}{30}$ $\dfrac{16}{100}$ $\dfrac{32}{50}$

$\dfrac{28}{30}$ $\dfrac{14}{15}$ $\dfrac{16}{28}$ $\dfrac{48}{84}$

$\dfrac{66}{100}$ $\dfrac{2}{3}$ $\dfrac{4}{16}$ $\dfrac{5}{25}$

$\dfrac{9}{12}$ $\dfrac{27}{36}$ $\dfrac{36}{20}$ $\dfrac{54}{30}$

2 Solve the proportions. Leave answers as improper fractions where appropriate.

$\dfrac{x}{60} = \dfrac{1}{5}$ $\dfrac{2}{17} = \dfrac{x}{8}$ $\dfrac{11}{x} = \dfrac{5}{7}$ $\dfrac{5}{9} = \dfrac{10}{x}$

$\dfrac{x}{100} = \dfrac{1}{3}$ $\dfrac{7}{13} = \dfrac{x}{39}$ $\dfrac{18}{x} = \dfrac{2}{3}$ $\dfrac{18}{5} = \dfrac{54}{x}$

Horizons Pre-Algebra, Tests and Resources

Percents

 Solve.

What is 40% of 90? What is 35% of 92? What is 36% of 40?

What is 8% of 50? What is 1.8% of 60? What is 210% of 80?

25 is 20% of what number? 66 is 40% of what number? 30 is 150% of what number?

30 is what percent of 120? 75 is what percent of 60? 9 is what percent of 72?

What is $33.\overline{3}$% of 66? What is $66.\overline{6}$% of 96? What is $16.\overline{6}$% of 42?

What is $83.\overline{3}$% of 54? What is 1.5% of 40? What is 240% of 120?

36 is 75% of what number? 62 is 50% of what number? 75 is 120% of what number?

Fraction to Percent Conversions, Percent Decrease

1 Complete the fraction-percent conversions.

Fraction	Percent
	25%
	33.$\overline{3}$%
	20%
	10%
	60%
	83.$\overline{3}$%
	62.5%
	90%
	87.5%

Percent	Fraction
	$\frac{2}{3}$
	$\frac{2}{5}$
	$\frac{1}{6}$
	$\frac{1}{8}$
	$\frac{3}{4}$
	$\frac{3}{10}$
	$\frac{4}{5}$
	$\frac{7}{10}$
	$\frac{3}{8}$

2 Find the percent decrease.

Original amount: 50
New amount: 30
Percent decrease:

Original amount: 80
New amount: 70
Percent decrease:

Original amount: 75
New amount: 50
Percent decrease:

Original amount: 30
New amount: 25
Percent decrease:

Original amount: 64
New amount: 40
Percent decrease:

Original amount: 42
New amount: 7
Percent decrease:

Mark-up and Discount

1 Calculate the sale price, given the percent discount.

Original Price	Percent Discount	Sale Price
$15	20%	
$20	15%	
$25	30%	
$30	33.$\overline{3}$%	
$40	40%	
$50	25%	

2 Calculate the new price, given the percent mark-up.

Original Price	Percent Mark-up	New Price
$15	20%	
$20	15%	
$25	30%	
$30	33.$\overline{3}$%	
$40	40%	
$50	25%	

Discount and Mark-up

 Calculate the sale price, given the percent discount.

Original Price	Percent Discount	Sale Price
$10	25%	
$20	30%	
$25	20%	
$30	66.$\overline{6}$%	
$40	15%	
$50	40%	

2 Calculate the new price, given the percent mark-up.

Original Price	Percent Mark-up	New Price
$10	25%	
$20	30%	
$25	20%	
$30	66.$\overline{6}$%	
$40	15%	
$50	40%	

Horizons Pre-Algebra, Tests and Resources

Simple Interest

1 Identify what each variable represents in the formula *i=Prt.*

i _____

P _____

r _____

t _____

2 Complete the chart to reflect simple interest.

Principal	Interest rate	Time in years	Amount of interest
$100	4.5%	2	
$500	7%	4	
$1,000	5%	3	
$5,000	8%	5	
$10,000	6%	10	
$15,000	11%	9	
$20,000	10%	6	
$25,000	0.5%	7	

3 For each loan in the chart above, find the total amount owed, including all interest.

Principal	Interest rate	Time in years	Total amount owed
$100	4.5%	2	
$500	7%	4	
$1,000	5%	3	
$5,000	8%	5	
$10,000	6%	10	
$15,000	11%	9	
$20,000	10%	6	
$25,000	0.5%	7	

Horizons Pre-Algebra, Tests and Resources

Pictographs

1 Complete the chart to show the number of brothers and sisters each classmate has.
If you have more than 10 classmates, choose any 10 for this project.

Name	Brothers	Sisters

Name	Brothers	Sisters

2 Draw a pictograph to show the information collected in the charts above.

Compound Interest

1 Identify what each variable represents in the formula $A = P(1 + r)^t$

A _____

P _____

r _____

t _____

2 Complete the chart to reflect interest compounded annually. You may use your calculator.
Round all answers to the nearest cent.

Principal	Interest rate	Time in years	Interest compounded annually
$100	0.5%	2	
$500	2.5%	4	
$1,000	5%	3	
$5,000	6%	5	
$10,000	8%	10	
$15,000	10%	9	
$20,000	11%	6	
$25,000	15%	7	

3 Complete the chart to reflect interest compounded quarterly. You may use your calculator.
Round all answers to the nearest cent.

Principal	Interest rate	Time in years	Interest compounded quarterly
$100	0.5%	2	
$500	2.5%	4	
$1,000	5%	3	
$5,000	6%	5	
$10,000	8%	10	
$15,000	10%	9	
$20,000	11%	6	
$25,000	15%	7	

Horizons Pre-Algebra, Tests and Resources

Mean, Median

1 Complete the chart.

Given Values	Values from Smallest to Largest	Sum	Mean	Median
10, 24, 26, 14, 17, 20, 21				
10.7, 24.5, 26.1, 37.1, 19.7				
51, 37, 44, 33, 45, 35				
51.2, 37.4, 44.2, 45.3				
98, 85, 75, 92				
89, 64, 57, 58, 46				
79, 82, 54, 94				
37.24, 44.21, 33.23				
17.13, 7.30, 23.37, 6.28				

2 Find the grade point average.

To calculate grade point averages, first assign a numerical value to each letter grade as follows: an A is worth 4.000, a B is worth 3.000, a C is worth 2.000, and a D is worth 1.000 on a 4-point scale. Then find the mean of the numerical values of the letter grades.

What is your grade point average if you have 5 A's and 2 B's?

What is your grade point average if you have 2 A's and 3 B's and 1 C?

Horizons Pre-Algebra, Tests and Resources

Pictographs, Circle Graphs

 Follow the directions.

Duane has made 5 videos about doing magic tricks with silks, 4 videos about doing magic tricks with various items, 8 videos about using magic tricks to teach biblical truths, and 1 video of magic tricks for kids. Draw a pictograph to show how many of each type of video Duane has made.

Make a circle graph showing the distribution of the types of videos Duane has made.

Frequency Distribution

1 For each set of numbers, make a frequency distribution and find the mean, median, and mode. Round answers to the nearest tenth where necessary.

6, 1, 5, 6, 3, 6, 4, 4, 3, 4, 2, 5, 4, 4, 1, 4, 3, 2, 3, 6

3, 1, 3, 3, 6, 2, 3, 4, 3, 4, 1, 6, 4, 5, 1, 6, 3, 6, 2, 1

Horizons Pre-Algebra, Tests and Resources

Probabilities

1 Find the probabilities.

A card game has cards numbered 1-14 in each of 4 different colors (red, yellow, green, and black). Find each of the following probabilities assuming the entire deck is used for each problem.

What is the probability of drawing a black card?

What is the probability of drawing an odd red card?

What is the probability of drawing a 10?

What is the probability of drawing a card that is a multiple of 3?

What is the probability of drawing a blue card?

What is the probability of drawing the green 7 card?

You have drawn 14 cards and do not have the black 11. What is the probability that the next card will be the black 11?

You have drawn 12 cards and have 2 cards that are green. What is the probability that the next card will be green?

Horizons Pre-Algebra, Tests and Resources

Stem-and-Leaf Plot, Histogram

 Find the median, mode(s), and range; make a stem-and-leaf plot, and draw a histogram.

The basketball scores for the most recent games of the NCAA top 25 teams were 72, 72, 89, 82, 72, 64, 90, 73, 71, 71, 77, 87, 71, 68, 63, 51, 91, 73, 73, 82, 76, 91, 69, 83, and 63.

Horizons Pre-Algebra, Tests and Resources

Probability, Odds

 1 Complete the chart to show probability and odds.

Scenario	Number of Possible Outcomes	Desired Event (E)	P (E)	Odds (in favor of E)	Odds (Against E)
Flipping a coin once		Heads			
Rolling a 6-sided die once		5			
Rolling a 6-sided die once		Even number			
Rolling a 6-sided die once		Multiple of 3			
Choosing an integer from 1 to 25		7			
Choosing an integer from 1 to 25		Even number			
Choosing an integer from 1 to 25		Multiple of 3			
Choosing an integer from 1 to 25		Multiple of 5			

Probability, Odds

 Complete the chart to show probability and odds.

Scenario	Number of Possible Outcomes	Desired Event (E)	P (E)	Odds (in favor of E)	Odds (Against E)
Flipping a coin once		Tails			
Rolling a 6-sided die once		2			
Rolling a 6-sided die once		Odd number			
Rolling a 6-sided die once		Prime number			
Choosing an integer from 1 to 25		10			
Choosing an integer from 1 to 25		Odd number			
Choosing an integer from 1 to 25		Multiple of 4			
Choosing an integer from 1 to 25		Prime number			

Probabilities

1 Find the probabilities.

In each of the following questions, game dice refer to standard 6-sided game dice.

What is the probability of rolling a 4 on one roll of one die?

What is the probability of rolling two 4's on one roll of two dice?

What is the probability of rolling all odd numbers on one roll of 3 dice?

What is the probability of rolling five 3's on one roll of five dice?

If you roll a 2, 3, 4, and 5 with four dice, what is the probability that a fifth die will be a 1 or a 6?

What is the probability of rolling 5 dice and getting numbers whose sum is 3?

What is the probability of rolling a single die three times and getting an odd number on the first roll, an even number on the second roll, and a prime number on the third roll?

If you roll two dice, what is the probability of getting numbers whose sum is 7?

Expected Values

 Complete the charts to find the expected value.

A game of chance costs $1 to play. A player selects five unique numbers from the set 1 – 39. If a player matches two to five of the selected numbers, he wins according to the chart below. Otherwise he loses his dollar. What is the expected value of the winnings? Is it a wise idea to play this game? Why or why not? (Keep in mind that multiple players matching all 5 numbers must split the highest prize amount.)

x	P(x)	xP(x)
Match 5: $50,000		
Match 4: $128		
Match 3: $8		
Match 2: $1		
Lose: -$1		

When there is no winner for a drawing, the prize values increase. After 5 consecutive days of no winners, the prize values had increased according to the chart below. Find the expected value of the current drawing. Is it a wise idea to play this game now? Why or why not? (Keep in mind that multiple players matching all 5 numbers must split the highest prize amount.)

x	P(x)	xP(x)
Match 5: $750,000		
Match 4: $181		
Match 3: $9		
Match 2: $1		
Lose: -$1		

Probabilities

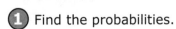 Find the probabilities.

The pep band has 16 seventh graders and 20 eighth graders. There are 18 boys and 18 girls in the pep band, and 6 of the girls are in seventh grade. If a student is selected at random, what is the probability that the student will be in seventh grade or a girl?

What is the probability that the student will be in eighth grade or a girl?

When rolling a standard 6-sided game die, what is the probability of rolling a 2 or a 3?

What is the probability of rolling a 4 or an odd number?

A pile of coins contains 7 each of pennies, nickels, dime, and quarters. If two coins are selected at random, what is the probability they will be worth a total of 26 cents?

If two coins are selected at random, what is the probability they will be worth a total of 50 cents?

Perimeter and Area of Rectangles and Squares

1 Complete the chart for rectangles.

Short side	Long side	Perimeter	Area
8 cm	10 cm		
	11 ft.		77 sq. ft.
	4.1 in.	11.2 in.	
3.3 km			22.77 km²
$3\frac{1}{2}$ m		$16\frac{1}{2}$ m	
$2\frac{1}{4}$ yd.	$5\frac{1}{3}$ yd.		

2 Complete the chart for squares.

Side	Perimeter	Area
8 cm		
		49 sq. ft.
	6 in.	
		10.89 km²
	14 m	
$2\frac{1}{4}$ yd.		

Perimeter and Area of Parallelograms

1 Complete the chart.

Figure	Drawing	Symbol
	•H	
Line *TV*		
		$\overline{RT}$
Ray *WX*		
	P∠	
		m ∥ *n*

2 Find the perimeter and area of each figure.

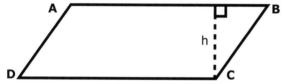

Given: □*ABCD*; *AB* = 20; *BC* = 10; *h* = 6

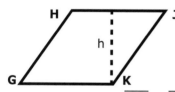

Given: □*GHJK*; $\overline{GH}$ ≅ $\overline{HJ}$; *GH* = 8; *h* = 6

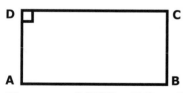

Given: □*ABCD*; *DC* = 9; *CB* = 5

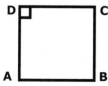

Given: □*ABCD*; *DC* = 11; *CB* = 11

Perimeter and Area of Triangles and Trapezoids

1 Find the perimeter and area of each figure.

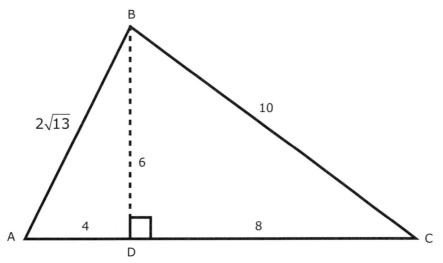

Triangle	Perimeter	Area
△ABD		
△BDC		
△ABC		

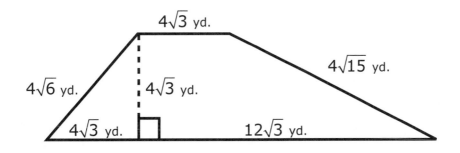

Perimeter:

Area:

Congruent Triangles

 Identify whether or not each pair of triangles is congruent based on the information given. If they are congruent, write the congruence statement, paying careful attention to the order of the letters. Tell which congruence pattern applies.

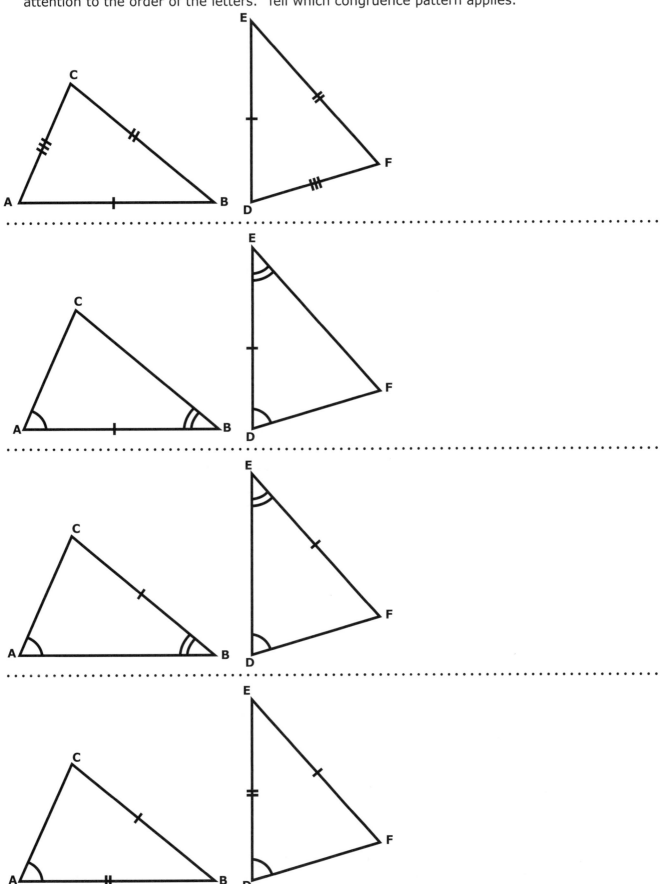

Symmetry, Congruent Triangles

1 Draw a line of symmetry in the figure below.

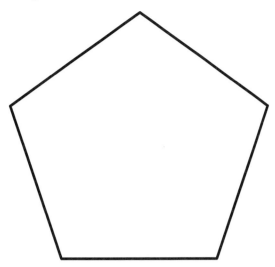

2 List the four congruence patterns for congruent triangles. For each congruence pattern, draw and label a pair of congruent triangles.

Lateral Area, Surface Area, Volume

 Solve.

A prism is 12 inches tall and has a square base whose sides are each 10 inches.

What is the lateral area of the prism?

What is the surface area of the prism?

What is the volume of the prism?

If a pyramid has the same base and height, what is the volume of the pyramid?

The slant height of the pyramid is 13 inches. What is the lateral area of the pyramid?

What is the surface area of the pyramid?

Lateral Area, Surface Area, Volume

 Solve.
A prism is 4 inches tall and has a square base whose sides are each 6 inches.

What is the lateral area of the prism?

What is the surface area of the prism?

What is the volume of the prism?

If a pyramid has the same base and height, what is the volume of the pyramid?

The slant height of the pyramid is 5 inches. What is the lateral area of the pyramid?

What is the surface area of the pyramid?

Lateral Area, Surface Area, Volume

 Solve.

A cylinder is 12 inches tall and has a base whose diameter is 10 inches.

What is the lateral area of the cylinder?

What is the surface area of the cylinder?

What is the volume of the cylinder?

If a cone has the same base and height, what is the volume of the cone?

The slant height of the cone is 13 inches. What is the lateral area of the cone?

What is the surface area of the cone?

Area, Volume

1 Solve.

Geocaching is like a treasure hunt using a GPS (global positioning system) receiver. If a GPS receiver is accurate to within 3 meters, what is the area of the region you will have to search for a hidden geocache once the receiver has led you to the location?

A geocache is a box that contains a logbook and various treasures. If the geocache box is 3 inches wide, 12 inches long, and 8 inches tall, what is the volume of the geocache?

A logbook in the geocache is 4 inches wide, 6 inches tall, and ½ inch thick. What is the volume of the logbook?

When the logbook is in the geocache, what is the volume of the remaining empty space?

A geocoin is a trackable coin that is moved from one geocache to another. The coin is 1 inch in diameter. What is the circumference of the geocoin? Use 3.14 as the value of π.

What is the area of one side of the geocoin? Use 3.14 as the value of π.

The geocoin is 1/8 inch thick. Find the volume of the geocoin. Use 3.14 as the value of π. Round your answer to the nearest hundredth.

Mass, Weight, Density

1 Use the formula $m = \frac{w}{g}$ to find the mass or weight of each item.

	Offset duplicator	Digital printing press	Short run color printer
Mass		7100 kg	
Weight	7644 kg • m/s²		47,530 kg • m/s²
Gravity	9.8 m/s²	9.8 m/s²	9.8 m/s²

2 Use the formula $d = \frac{m}{v}$ to find the density of each object and identify if it will float in pure water. The density of pure water is 1000 kg/m³.

Substance	Mass	Volume	Density	Float: Y/N
Crushed asphalt	504.7 kg	0.7 m³		
Baking powder	742.63 kg	1.03 m³		
Beeswax	2114.2 kg	2.2 m³		
Window glass	206.32 kg	0.08 m³		

Circle Terminology, Parallel and Skew Lines

1 In the circle below, draw and label the following parts: tangent, chord, diameter, radius, central angle, and secant.

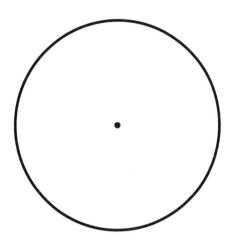

2 Identify parallel and skew edges.

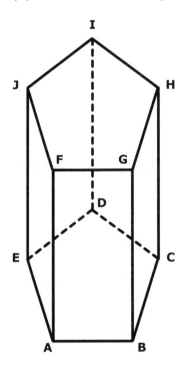

List all pairs of parallel edges.

For each edge, list all the skew lines.

Points, Lines

1 Answer the questions. Draw a picture to illustrate your answer.
How many lines can be drawn between two points?

How many points can be drawn on a single line?

How many lines can be drawn through a single point?

2 Mark the diagram according to the instructions.

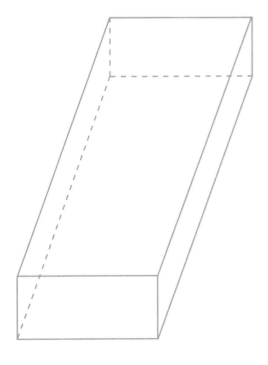

Color one set of parallel lines red.
Color one set of intersecting lines blue.
Color one set of skew lines green.

Complementary, Supplementary, and Vertical Angles

1 Identify each angle as acute, right, obtuse, or straight. Find the measure of the complementary and supplementary angles, if applicable, for each given angle.

19°   136°

167°   180°

71°   2°

2 Use the diagram below to answer the questions.

List 8 pairs of complementary angles.

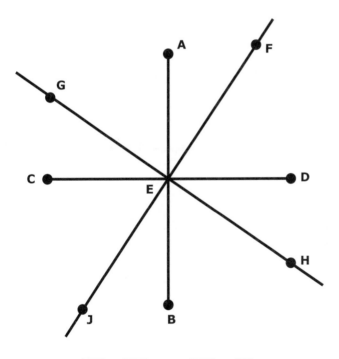

$\overline{AB} \perp \overline{CD}$ and $\overline{GH} \perp \overline{JF}$

List each straight angle using three letters.

Graphing Linear Equations

1 Graph the following equations on your own graph paper.

$y = 2x$

$y = -2x$

$y = -3x$

$y = x + 1$

$y = x - 4$

$y = x - 1$

$y = 2x - 1$

$y = 2x + 3$

$y = 3x - 3$

$y = 2(x - 2)$

$y = 3(x - 3)$

$y = 2(x - 1)$

Quadrants, Graphing Linear Equations

1 Give the coordinates for each point and identify the quadrant.

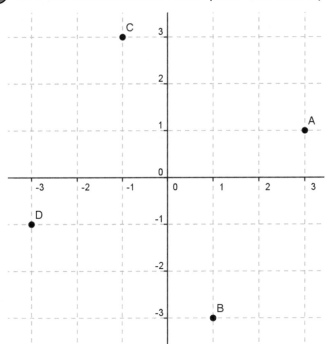

2 Find three possible solutions for each equation and draw the graph on your own graph paper.

$$y = -x \qquad\qquad y = 2x - 1 \qquad\qquad y = 3(x - 1)$$

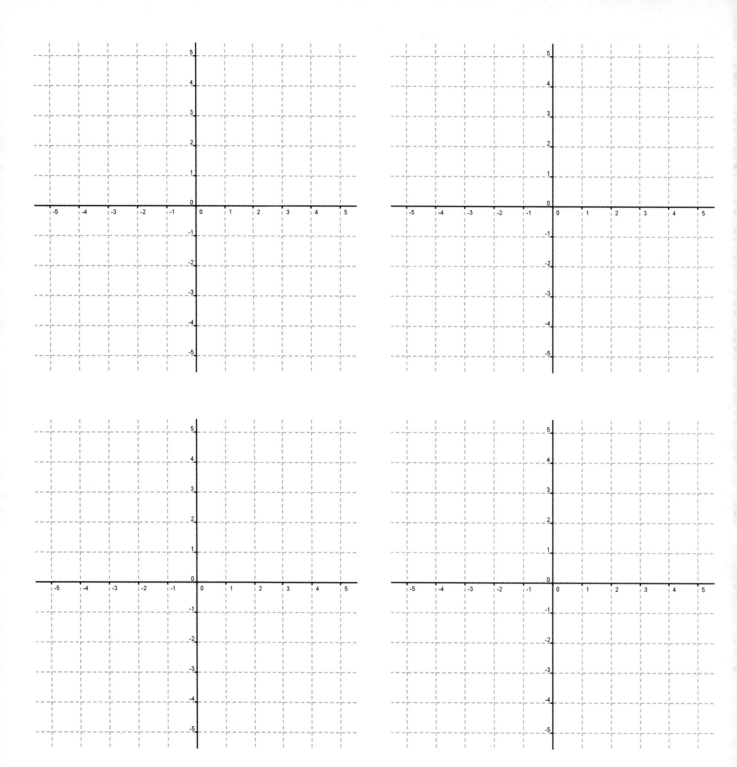

Horizons Pre-Algebra, Tests and Resources

Graphing Inequalities, Slope

1 Graph the inequalities.

$y < -x$

$y > 2x - 1$

$y \leq 3(x - 1)$

2 Find the slope of the line joining the points.

(1, 5) and (3, 6)

(2, 4) and (7, 3)

(3, -1) and (2, 3)

(-1, -2) and (-2, -4)

3 Find the slope of each line.

$x + y - 5 = 0$

$2x + y - 3 = 0$

$-x + y - 5 = 0$

$-3x + y - 4 = 0$

$-2x + y + 7 = 0$

$3x + y - 1 = 0$

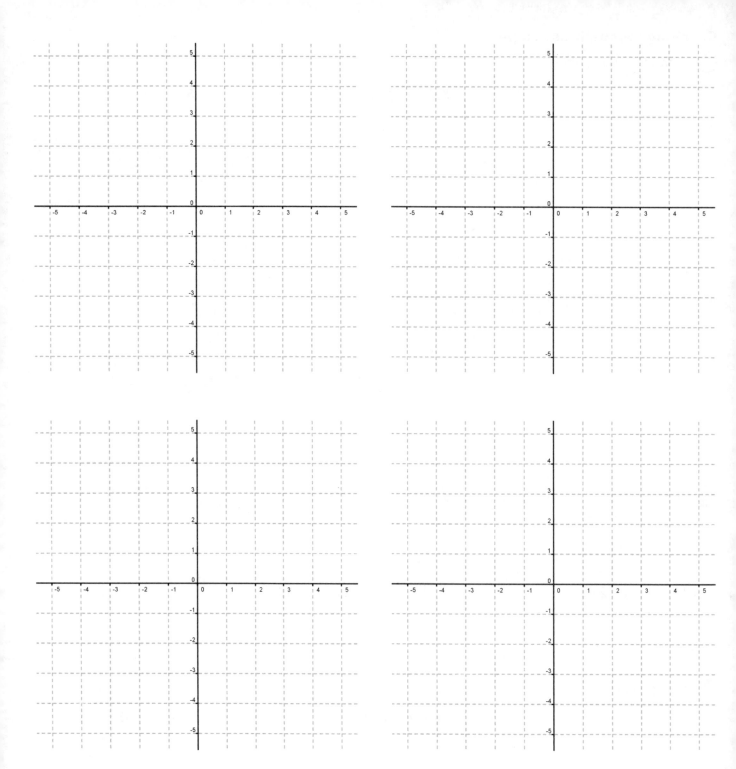

172   *Horizons Pre-Algebra, Tests and Resources*

Slope

1 Find the slope of the line joining the points.

(1, 5) and (4, 2)   (1, 5) and (7, 5)

(3, -1) and (3, 5)   (3, -1) and (3, 3)

(1, 5) and (7, 2)   (1, 6) and (2, 5)

(3, -1) and (4, 1)   (3, -1) and (-2, -3)

2 Find the slope of each line.

$x + y - 6 = 0$ $3x + y - 1 = 0$ $-x + y + 3 = 0$

$-3x + y - 7 = 0$ $-2x + y + 1 = 0$ $4x + y - 2 = 0$

$2x + y - 5 = 0$ $4x + y - 3 = 0$ $-3x + y - 5 = 0$

$-2x + y - 4 = 0$ $-5x + y + 7 = 0$ $6x + y - 5 = 0$

Solve Systems of Equations

 Solve the systems of equations. Express each answer as a coordinate point.

$3x + y + 5 = 0$
$-4x + y - 2 = 0$

$x - 2y + 2 = 0$
$-2x + 2y - 5 = 0$

$-3x - y + 3 = 0$
$3x - 2y - 6 = 0$

$-3x + 2y - 5 = 0$
$4x + 2y + 2 = 0$

$x - 3y + 2 = 0$
$-2x + 3y - 5 = 0$

$-x + y - 2 = 0$
$2x - y + 5 = 0$

$x - 5y + 2 = 0$
$-2x + 5y - 5 = 0$

$2x + y + 2 = 0$
$-2x + y - 2 = 0$

$3x - 3y + 6 = 0$
$-2x + y - 5 = 0$

Horizons Pre-Algebra, Tests and Resources

1 Convert to degrees Celsius. Round answers to the nearest tenth.

125°F   80°F   55°F

90°F   120°F   115°F

2 Convert to degrees Fahrenheit.

125°C   80°C   55°C

90°C   120°C   115°C

3 Solve.

Convert 16 ounces to milliliters.

Convert 6 quarts to liters.

Convert 18 gallons to liters.

Convert 150 milliliters to ounces.

Convert 7 liters to quarts.

Convert 19 liters to gallons.

Convert 2900 milliliters to quarts.

Convert 125 ounces to liters.

Convert 1700 milliliters to gallons.

1 Complete the chart to convert from degrees Fahrenheit to degrees Celsius. Round answers to the nearest tenth where necessary.

°F	°C
20°	
25°	
30°	
35°	
40°	
45°	
50°	

2 Complete the chart to convert from degrees Celsius to degrees Fahrenheit.

°C	°F
20°	
25°	
30°	
35°	
40°	
45°	
50°	

3 Solve.

Convert 16 ounces to milliliters.	Convert 2 quarts to liters.	Convert 20 gallons to liters.
Convert 150 milliliters to ounces.	Convert 2 liters to quarts.	Convert 15 liters to gallons.
Convert 2000 milliliters to quarts.	Convert 150 ounces to liters.	Convert 2500 milliliters to gallons.

30—60—90 Triangles

1 Label the missing sides in each of the triangles below.

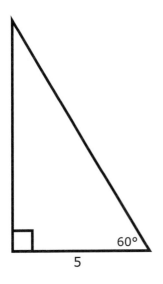

5

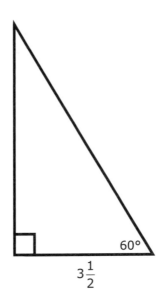

$3\frac{1}{2}$

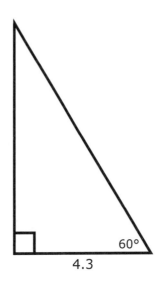

4.3

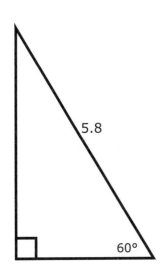

5.8   60°

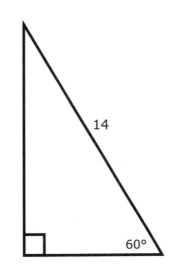

14   60°

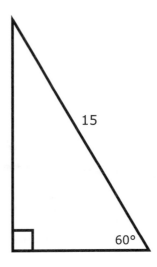

15   60°

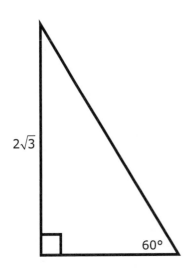

$2\sqrt{3}$ 60°

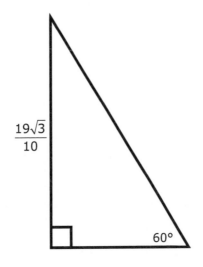

$\frac{19\sqrt{3}}{10}$ 60°

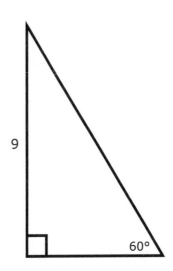

9   60°

Label the missing sides in each of the triangles below.

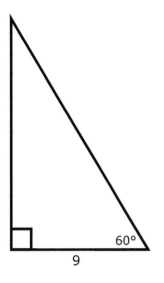

9

60°

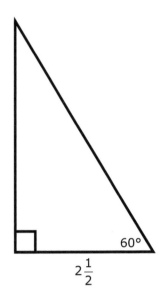

60°

$2\frac{1}{2}$

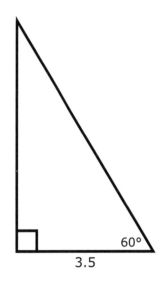

60°

3.5

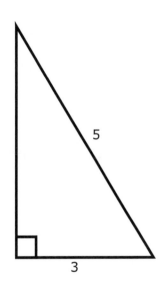

5

3

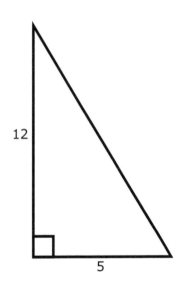

12

5

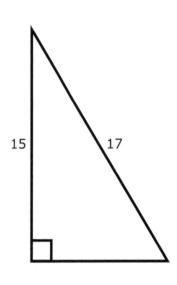

15

17

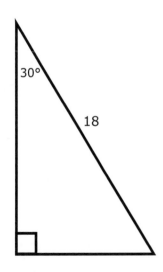

30°

18

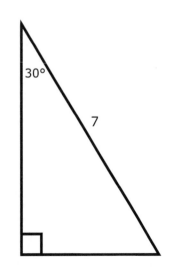

30°

7

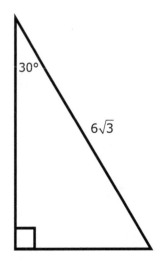

30°

$6\sqrt{3}$

1 Label the missing sides in each of the triangles below.

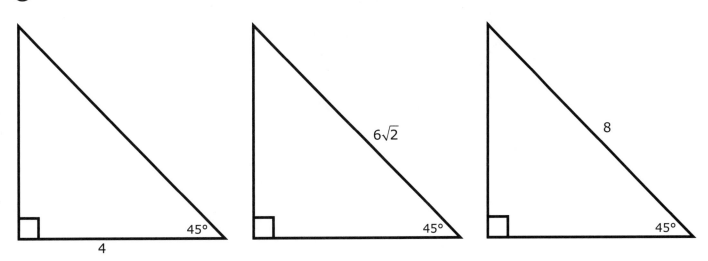

2 Label the missing sides and find the sine and cosine of each acute angle.

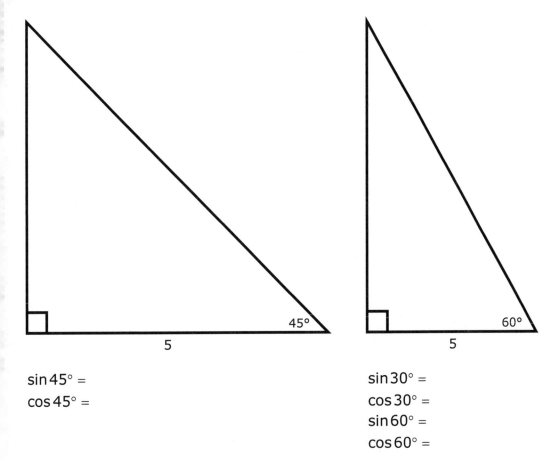

$\sin 45° =$

$\cos 45° =$

$\sin 30° =$

$\cos 30° =$

$\sin 60° =$

$\cos 60° =$

Adding Polynomials

1 Add.

$$3x^2 + 4x + 1$$
$$+\ 2x^2 + 4x + 3$$

$$9x^2 + 5x + 3$$
$$+x^2 - 3x - 2$$

$$4x^2 - 5x + 6$$
$$+3x^2 + 2x - 4$$

$$7x^2 + 4x + 3$$
$$+\ 5x^2 + 3x + 6$$

$$3x^2 + 5x + 5$$
$$+4x^2 - 9x - 7$$

$$3x^2 - 5x + 8$$
$$+11x^2 + 2x - 4$$

$$3x^2 + 5x + 7$$
$$+\ 2x^2 + 6x + 4$$

$$3x^2 + 4x + 8$$
$$+x^2 - 7x - 9$$

$$3x^2 - 5x + 4$$
$$+4x^2 + 9x - 7$$

2 Write the problem vertically and add.

$$\left(3x^2 + 4x + 2\right) + \left(x^2 + 5x + 4\right) =$$

$$\left(6x^2 + 5x + 7\right) + \left(3x^2 + 4x + 8\right) =$$

$$\left(2x^2 + 7x + 4\right) + \left(5x^2 - 9x + 2\right) =$$

$$\left(2x^2 + 7x - 6\right) + \left(5x^2 - 3x + 7\right) =$$

$$\left(7x^2 - 5x + 4\right) + \left(-x^2 + 6x - 2\right) =$$

$$\left(9x^2 + 2x + 9\right) + \left(-8x^2 - 4x - 5\right) =$$

$$\left(3x^2 + 2x + 7\right) + \left(x^2 + 9x + 8\right) =$$

$$\left(9x^2 + 7x + 9\right) + \left(2x^2 + 9x + 8\right) =$$

$$\left(6x^2 + 7x + 3\right) + \left(5x^2 - 4x + 8\right) =$$

$$\left(7x^2 + 3x - 5\right) + \left(4x^2 - 9x + 3\right) =$$

Types of Polynomials

1 Identify whether or not each expression is a polynomial. If it is not a polynomial, tell why not. For each polynomial, identify it as a constant, monomial, binomial, or trinomial. Questions may have more than one answer.

$4x - 7$

12

$5x^2 + \frac{3}{x} - 4$

$x^{-2} - 1$

$x^2 - 2x + 1$

$7x - 2$

$4x^2 + \frac{6}{x} - 5$

$3x^{-2} + 2$

$4x^2 - 3x + 5$

$-7x$

Subtracting Polynomials

1 Subtract.

$$
\begin{aligned}
&\left(3x^2 + 4x + 1\right) \\
- \ &\left(2x^2 + 2x + 3\right) \\
\hline
\end{aligned}
\qquad
\begin{aligned}
&\left(9x^2 + 5x + 3\right) \\
- &\left(x^2 - 3x - 2\right) \\
\hline
\end{aligned}
\qquad
\begin{aligned}
&\left(4x^2 - 5x + 6\right) \\
- &\left(3x^2 + 2x - 4\right) \\
\hline
\end{aligned}
$$

$$
\begin{aligned}
&\left(7x^2 + 4x + 3\right) \\
- &\left(5x^2 + 3x + 6\right) \\
\hline
\end{aligned}
\qquad
\begin{aligned}
&\left(3x^2 + 5x + 5\right) \\
- &\left(4x^2 - 9x - 7\right) \\
\hline
\end{aligned}
\qquad
\begin{aligned}
&\left(3x^2 - 5x + 8\right) \\
- &\left(11x^2 + 2x - 4\right) \\
\hline
\end{aligned}
$$

$$
\begin{aligned}
&\left(3x^2 + 5x + 7\right) \\
- &\left(2x^2 + 6x + 4\right) \\
\hline
\end{aligned}
\qquad
\begin{aligned}
&\left(3x^2 + 4x + 8\right) \\
- \ &\left(x^2 - 7x - 9\right) \\
\hline
\end{aligned}
\qquad
\begin{aligned}
&\left(3x^2 - 5x + 4\right) \\
- &\left(4x^2 + 9x - 7\right) \\
\hline
\end{aligned}
$$

2 Write the problem vertically and subtract.

$$\left(3x^2 + 4x + 2\right) - \left(x^2 + 5x + 4\right) = \qquad\qquad \left(6x^2 + 5x + 7\right) - \left(3x^2 + 4x + 8\right) =$$

$$\left(2x^2 + 7x + 4\right) - \left(5x^2 - 9x + 2\right) = \qquad\qquad \left(2x^2 + 7x - 6\right) - \left(5x^2 - 3x + 7\right) =$$

$$\left(7x^2 - 5x + 4\right) - \left(-x^2 + 6x - 2\right) = \qquad\qquad \left(9x^2 + 2x + 9\right) - \left(-8x^2 - 4x - 5\right) =$$

$$\left(3x^2 + 2x + 7\right) - \left(x^2 + 9x + 8\right) = \qquad\qquad \left(9x^2 + 7x + 9\right) - \left(2x^2 + 9x + 8\right) =$$

Addition and Subtraction of Polynomials

Worksheet 68

1 Add.

$$8x^2 + 4x + 6$$
$$+ \ 2x^2 + 6x + 5$$

$$3x^2 + 2x + 7$$
$$+x^2 - 3x - 5$$

$$2x^2 - 4x + 7$$
$$+6x^2 + 5x - 1$$

$$6x^2 + 4x + 2$$
$$+ \ 7x^2 + 2x + 5$$

$$5x^2 + 4x + 7$$
$$+6x^2 - 5x - 8$$

$$9x^2 - 4x + 3$$
$$+5x^2 + 6x - 1$$

$$3x^2 + 4x + 8$$
$$+ \ 6x^2 + 2x + 7$$

$$7x^2 + 5x + 3$$
$$+x^2 - 4x - 6$$

$$7x^2 - 5x + 8$$
$$+3x^2 + 4x - 6$$

$$2x^2 + 9x + 2$$
$$+ \ 3x^2 + 4x + 8$$

$$2x^2 + 5x + 8$$
$$+x^2 - 4x - 7$$

$$7x^2 - 5x + 6$$
$$+8x^2 + 2x - 8$$

2 Subtract.

$$\left(9x^2 + 7x + 8\right)$$
$$- \ \left(6x^2 + 5x + 4\right)$$

$$\left(7x^2 + 5x + 6\right)$$
$$-\left(x^2 - 5x - 4\right)$$

$$\left(6x^2 - 4x + 5\right)$$
$$-\left(2x^2 + 7x - 6\right)$$

$$\left(5x^2 + 7x + 8\right)$$
$$-\left(3x^2 + 5x + 4\right)$$

$$\left(2x^2 + 4x + 7\right)$$
$$-\left(4x^2 - 5x - 9\right)$$

$$\left(5x^2 - 7x + 3\right)$$
$$-\left(7x^2 + 6x - 4\right)$$

$$\left(2x^2 + 4x + 5\right)$$
$$-\left(3x^2 + 8x + 7\right)$$

$$\left(7x^2 + 2x + 4\right)$$
$$- \ \left(x^2 - 5x - 8\right)$$

$$\left(7x^2 - 2x + 4\right)$$
$$-\left(5x^2 + 7x - 8\right)$$

$$\left(2x^2 + 7x + 5\right)$$
$$-\left(6x^2 + 5x + 8\right)$$

$$\left(5x^2 + 6x + 8\right)$$
$$- \ \left(x^2 - 5x - 1\right)$$

$$\left(2x^2 - 6x + 7\right)$$
$$-\left(5x^2 + 2x - 3\right)$$

Horizons Pre-Algebra, Tests and Resources   193

Multiplication and Division of Polynomials

1 Multiply.

$4x\left(7xy^2\right)$ $\qquad$ $5x^2\left(7x^2y^2\right)$ $\qquad$ $9x\left(6x^2+x-3\right)$

$5x^2\left(3xy^2\right)$ $\qquad$ $3x^3\left(6x^2y^2\right)$ $\qquad$ $3x\left(4x^2-2x+3\right)$

$x^3\left(5xy^2\right)$ $\qquad$ $2x^3\left(9x^2y^4\right)$ $\qquad$ $4x\left(2x^2-3x+7\right)$

$x^3\left(11xy^2\right)$ $\qquad$ $10x^3\left(4x^2y^4\right)$ $\qquad$ $6x\left(3x^2-5x+4\right)$

2 Divide.

$5x^5\div x^3$ $\qquad$ $12x^3y^2\div x^3$ $\qquad$ $9x^4y^3\div 9xy^2$

$7x^3\div x$ $\qquad$ $6xy^2\div 2x$ $\qquad$ $22x^3y^3\div 2x^2y^2$

$16y^4\div 8y^2$ $\qquad$ $18x^2y^3\div 6y^2$ $\qquad$ $24x^4y^2\div 8x^2y^2$

$12y^5\div 3y^2$ $\qquad$ $21x^3y^2\div 3y$ $\qquad$ $16x^5y^4\div 4x^2y^2$

$15y^7\div 5y^3$ $\qquad$ $24x^3y^4\div 4xy$ $\qquad$ $36x^5y^4\div 4x^2y^3$

Division of Polynomials, FOIL

1 Multiply, using the FOIL method.

$(x+2)(x+3)$ $\qquad\qquad\qquad\qquad$ $(x+4)(x-3)$

$(x+4)(x-1)$ $\qquad\qquad\qquad\qquad$ $(2x+5)(x-4)$

$(2x-3)(x-1)$ $\qquad\qquad\qquad\qquad$ $(2x+7)(3x-4)$

$(3x+1)(x-4)$ $\qquad\qquad\qquad\qquad$ $(2x-6)(4x+3)$

2 Divide.

$(x^2-5x+6)\div(x-2)$ $\qquad$ $(2x^2+5x+2)\div(x+2)$ $\qquad$ $(6x^2-7x+2)\div(3x-2)$

$(x^2+x-6)\div(x-2)$ $\qquad$ $(3x^2+4x-4)\div(x+2)$ $\qquad$ $(8x^2+10x-3)\div(2x+3)$

Division of Polynomials, FOIL

 Divide.

$$x + 2 \overline{\smash{)}\, x^2 + 6x + 8} \qquad\qquad x - 3 \overline{\smash{)}\, x^2 + 2x - 15} \qquad\qquad x - 7 \overline{\smash{)}\, 3x^2 - 19x - 14}$$

$$\left(x^2 + 15x + 54 \right) \div \left(x + 6 \right) \qquad \left(x^2 - 3x - 4 \right) \div \left(x + 1 \right) \qquad \left(6x^2 + x - 12 \right) \div \left(3x - 4 \right)$$

$$\left(3x^2 - 14x - 24 \right) \div \left(x - 6 \right) \qquad \left(2x^2 - 11x + 15 \right) \div \left(x - 3 \right) \qquad \left(10x^2 - 39x - 27 \right) \div \left(2x - 9 \right)$$

2 Multiply.

$$\left(x + 6 \right)\left(x - 7 \right) \qquad\qquad\qquad\qquad \left(2x + 5 \right)\left(3x - 8 \right)$$

$$\left(2x + 1 \right)\left(x - 6 \right) \qquad\qquad\qquad\qquad \left(2x - 5 \right)\left(4x + 3 \right)$$

Flips, Turns

1 Plot the given points in blue and join them to form a polygon. Graph the flip over the x-axis in green and the flip over the y-axis in red.

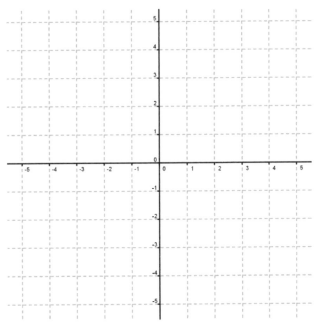

(1, 2), (3, 1), (4, 3), and (2, 4)

2 Plot the given points in blue and join them to form a polygon. Graph the turn 90° counterclockwise in green and the turn 90° clockwise in red.

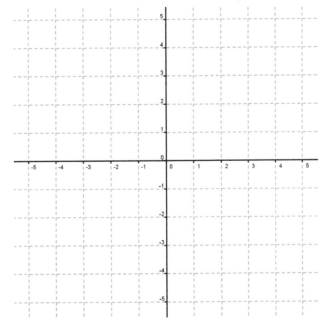

(1, 2), (3, 1), (4, 3), and (2, 4)

Flips, Turns, Slides

1 Plot the given points in blue and join them to form a polygon. Graph the flip over the *x*-axis in green and the flip over the *y*-axis in red.

(3, 1), (1, 3), and (2, 5)

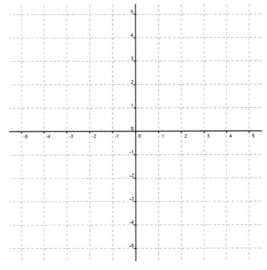

2 Plot the given points in blue and join them to form a polygon. Graph the turn 90° clockwise in green and the turn 90° counterclockwise in red

(3, 1), (1, 3), and (2, 5)

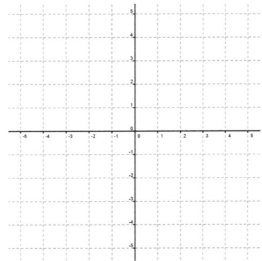

3 Plot the given points in blue and join them to form a polygon. Graph the slide down 4 units in green and the slide left 2 units in red.

(3, 1), (1, 3), and (2, 5)

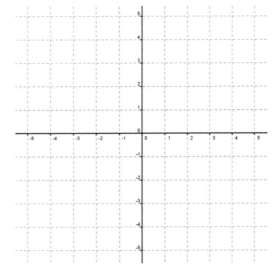

Reflections, Rotations, Scaling

1 Plot the given points in blue and join them to form a polygon. Graph the reflection over the *x*-axis in green and the reflection over the *y*-axis in red.

(2, 2), (2, 4), and (4, 0)

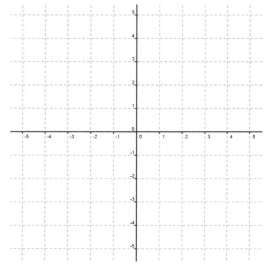

2 Plot the given points in blue and join them to form a polygon. Graph the rotation 90° clockwise in green and the rotation 90° counterclockwise in red.

(2, 2), (2, 4), and (4, 0)

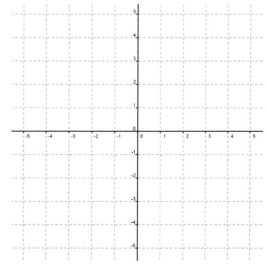

3 Plot the given points in blue and join them to form a polygon. Calculate the coordinates of the figure when you scale it by a factor of 0.5 and draw its graph in green. Calculate the coordinates of the figure when you scale it by a factor of 1.5 and draw its graph in red.

(2, 2), (2, 4), and (4, 0)

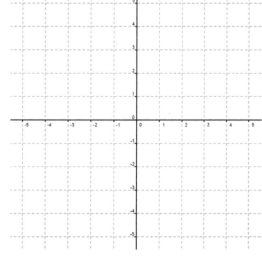

Review Terms

 Matching.

Write the letter of the correct term on the blank of each definition.

____ Fractions that have different numerators and denominators but are equal in value

____ A fraction whose numerator is greater than its denominator

____ The result of adding a whole number and a fraction

____ An expression that compares two quantities

____ A mathematical sentence showing two ratios are equal

____ A proportionally accurate representation of a real thing

____ A method of writing very large and very small numbers

____ Hundredth

____ The amount the price of an item is increased

____ The fee paid for the use of money

____ The amount of money borrowed or invested

____ The percent of the principal that is paid each term

____ Interest charged on the original amount of the principal

____ The amount a sales person earns based on a percent of the price of the item sold

____ The difference between an item's selling price and the costs incurred to sell the item

____ Payment for the use of property

____ Interest paid on the principle *and* the previously earned interest

Terms

A. Commission

B. Compound interest

C. Equivalent fractions

D. Improper fraction

E. Interest

F. Interest rate

G. Mark-up

H. Mixed number

I. Percent

J. Principal

K. Profit

L. Proportion

M. Ratio

N. Royalties

O. Scale drawing

P. Scientific notation

Q. Simple interest

Percent Problems

 Complete the chart for each scenario.

Waiters and waitresses generally earn 15% to 20% in tips based on the price of the food they serve. Calculate the amount each customer should leave as a tip. Round each answer to the nearest cent.

Amount of bill	15% tip	20% tip
$5.00		
$7.50		
$10.25		
$20.75		
$35.00		

You own a retail store and mark up the selling price to reflect a 30% increase over the whole-sale price. Calculate the selling price based on the given wholesale price, and then calculate the sale price if all items are marked 20% off. Round each answer to the nearest cent.

Wholesale price	Selling price	Sale price
$2.27		
$5.50		
$6.73		
$8.50		
$10.00		

If you had up to $8375 of taxable income as an individual in 2010, you owed 10% in income tax, 12.4% for Social Security, and 2.9% for Medicare. Calculate the amount of each tax. Round your answers to the nearest dollar.

Taxable Income	Income Tax	Social Security	Medicare
$1,500			
$2,775			
$5,800			
$7,900			
$8,375			

Permutations, Combinations

① Calculate the permutations and combinations.

p(7,2) =

p(5,3) =

p(9,4) =

p(6,2) =

p(8,3) =

p(6,4) =

p(7,5) =

C(7,2) =

C(5,3) =

C(9,4) =

C(6,2) =

C(8,3) =

C(6,4) =

C(7,5) =

Congruent Triangles

1 Mark each set of congruent sides and angles to show $\triangle ABC \cong \triangle DEF$.

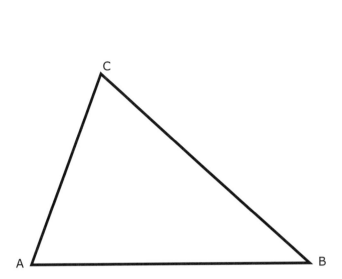 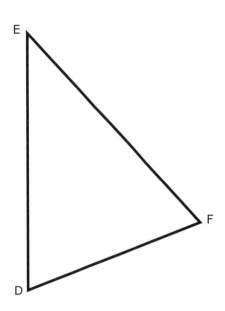

2 List four congruence patterns for triangles.

3 Explain why AAA and SSA do not prove congruence in triangles.

1 Solve.

The Daytona International Speedway is a 2.5-mile tri-oval track. If a race is 500 miles long, how many laps must each driver complete?

If a driver averages 175 miles per hour, how much driving time in hours will it take to complete the race? (Ignore time for pit road, cautions, etc.) Round your answer to the nearest hundredth.

The track is 40 feet wide with a 31° banking. How much higher is the top of the track than the bottom of the track? Hint: Use your calculator to find sin 31° to the nearest ten thousandth. Set up an equation to solve for the height.

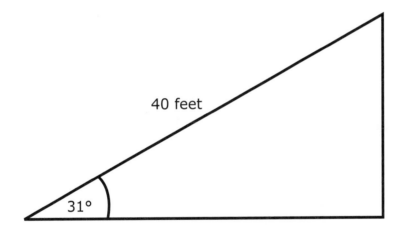

40 feet

31°

Solve.

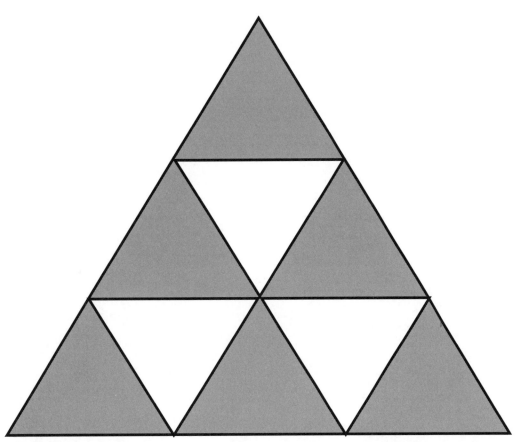

A large equilateral triangle contains 9 congruent equilateral triangles. If the length of each side of the large triangle is 6 inches, what is the area of the shaded region?

Horizons Pre-Algebra, Tests and Resources

Formula Strips

For use in Lesson 41

English length equivalents:
1 mile = 5280 feet
1 mile = 1760 yards
1 yard = 3 feet
1 yard = 36 inches

English-Metric length equivalents:
1 inch = 2.54 cm
1 inch = 25.4 mm
1 yard = 0.91 meter
1 mile = 1.61 km

Metric-English length equivalents:
1 cm = 0.39 inch
1 meter = 1.09 yards
1 km = 0.62 mile

- -

For use in Lesson 45

English length equivalents:
1 mile = 5280 feet
1 mile = 1760 yards
1 yard = 3 feet
1 yard = 36 inches

English-Metric length equivalents:
1 inch = 2.54 cm
1 inch = 25.4 mm
1 yard = 0.91 meter
1 mile = 1.61 km

Metric-English length equivalents:
1 cm = 0.39 inch
1 meter = 1.09 yards
1 km = 0.62 mile

- -

For use in Lesson 50

English length equivalents:
1 mile = 5280 feet
1 mile = 1760 yards
1 yard = 3 feet
1 yard = 36 inches

English-Metric length equivalents:
1 inch = 2.54 cm
1 inch = 25.4 mm
1 yard = 0.91 meter
1 mile = 1.61 km

Metric-English length equivalents:
1 cm = 0.39 inch
1 meter = 1.09 yards
1 km = 0.62 mile

- -

For use on Test 5

English length equivalents:
1 mile = 5280 feet
1 mile = 1760 yards
1 yard = 3 feet
1 yard = 36 inches

English-Metric length equivalents:
1 inch = 2.54 cm
1 inch = 25.4 mm
1 yard = 0.91 meter
1 mile = 1.61 km

Metric-English length equivalents:
1 cm = 0.39 inch
1 meter = 1.09 yards
1 km = 0.62 mile

Formula Strips

For use in Lesson 71

English length equivalents:
1 mile = 5280 feet
1 mile = 1760 yards
1 yard = 3 feet
1 yard = 36 inches

English-Metric length equivalents:
1 inch = 2.54 cm
1 inch = 25.4 mm
1 yard = 0.91 meter
1 mile = 1.61 km

Metric-English length equivalents:
1 cm = 0.39 inch
1 meter = 1.09 yards
1 km = 0.62 mile

For use in Lesson 74

English length equivalents:
1 mile = 5280 feet
1 mile = 1760 yards
1 yard = 3 feet
1 yard = 36 inches

English-Metric length equivalents:
1 inch = 2.54 cm
1 inch = 25.4 mm
1 yard = 0.91 meter
1 mile = 1.61 km

Metric-English length equivalents:
1 cm = 0.39 inch
1 meter = 1.09 yards
1 km = 0.62 mile

For use on Exam 2

English length equivalents:
1 mile = 5280 feet
1 mile = 1760 yards
1 yard = 3 feet
1 yard = 36 inches

English-Metric length equivalents:
1 inch = 2.54 cm
1 inch = 25.4 mm
1 yard = 0.91 meter
1 mile = 1.61 km

Metric-English length equivalents:
1 cm = 0.39 inch
1 meter = 1.09 yards
1 km = 0.62 mile

Formula Strips

For use in Lesson 85

English length equivalents:
1 mile = 5280 feet
1 mile = 1760 yards
1 yard = 3 feet
1 yard = 36 inches

English-Metric length equivalents:
1 inch = 2.54 cm
1 inch = 25.4 mm
1 yard = 0.91 meter
1 mile = 1.61 km

Metric-English length equivalents:
1 cm = 0.39 inch
1 meter = 1.09 yards
1 km = 0.62 mile

- -

For use in Lesson 87

English length equivalents:
1 mile = 5280 feet
1 mile = 1760 yards
1 yard = 3 feet
1 yard = 36 inches

English-Metric length equivalents:
1 inch = 2.54 cm
1 inch = 25.4 mm
1 yard = 0.91 meter
1 mile = 1.61 km

Metric-English length equivalents:
1 cm = 0.39 inch
1 meter = 1.09 yards
1 km = 0.62 mile

- -

For use in Lesson 88

English length equivalents:
1 mile = 5280 feet
1 mile = 1760 yards
1 yard = 3 feet
1 yard = 36 inches

English-Metric length equivalents:
1 inch = 2.54 cm
1 inch = 25.4 mm
1 yard = 0.91 meter
1 mile = 1.61 km

Metric-English length equivalents:
1 cm = 0.39 inch
1 meter = 1.09 yards
1 km = 0.62 mile

- -

For use on Test 9

Perimeter:
Parallelogram = $2\ell + 2w$
Rhombus = $4s$
Rectangle = $2\ell + 2w$
Square = $4s$
Triangle = $a + b + c$
Trapezoid = $a + b + c + d$

Area:
Parallelogram = bh
Rhombus = bh
Rectangle = bh
Square = s^2
Triangle = $\frac{1}{2}bh$
Trapezoid = $\frac{1}{2}(b_1 + b_2)h$

Circle:
Circumference = πd or $2\pi r$
Area = πr^2

Formula Strips

For use in Exam 3

Solid geometry:

Cylinder: $V = \pi r^2 h$

$LA = 2\pi rL$

$SA = 2\pi rL + 2\pi r^2$

Pyramid: $V = \frac{1}{3}Bh$

$LA = \frac{1}{2}PL$

$SA = \frac{1}{2}PL + B$

Sphere: $SA = 4\pi r^2$

$V = \frac{4}{3}\pi r^3$

Prism: $V = Bh$

$LA = PL$

$SA = PL + 2B$

Cone: $V = \frac{1}{3}\pi r^2 h$

$LA = \pi rL$

$SA = \pi rL + \pi r^2$

- -

For use in Lesson 122

English-metric liquid equivalents:
1 ounce (oz.) = 30 mL
1 quart (qt.) = 0.95 L
1 gallon (gal.) = 3.8 L

Metric-English liquid equivalents:
1 mL = 0.034 ounce
1 L = 1.06 quarts
1 L = 0.26 gallon

- -

For use in Lesson 123

Weight-mass equivalents:
1 ounce = 28.35 grams
1 pound = 0.454 kg
1 short ton = 907 kg

Mass-weight equivalents:
1 g = 0.035 ounces
1 kg = 2.2 pounds
1 metric ton = 1.1 S.ton

- -

For use in Lesson 130

English length equivalents:
1 mile = 5280 feet
1 mile = 1760 yards
1 yard = 3 feet
1 yard = 36 inches

English-Metric length equivalents:
1 inch = 2.54 cm
1 inch = 25.4 mm
1 yard = 0.91 meter
1 mile = 1.61 km

Metric-English length equivalents:
1 cm = 0.39 inch
1 meter = 1.09 yards
1 km = 0.62 mile

Formula Strips

For use on Test 13

English-metric liquid equivalents:
1 ounce (oz.) = 30 mL
1 quart (qt.) = 0.95 L
1 gallon (gal.) = 3.8 L

Weight-mass equivalents:
1 ounce = 28.35 grams
1 pound = 0.454 kg
1 short ton = 907 kg

Metric-English liquid equivalents:
1 mL = 0.034 ounce
1 L = 1.06 quarts
1 L = 0.26 gallon

Mass-weight equivalents:
1 g = 0.035 ounces
1 kg = 2.2 pounds
1 metric ton = 1.1 S.ton

For use in Lesson 134

Plane geometry:
Circles:
$C = 2\pi r$

$A = \pi r^2$

For use in Lesson 137

Plane geometry:
Circles:
$C = 2\pi r$
$A = \pi r^2$

For use in Lesson 139

Plane geometry:
Circles:
$C = 2\pi r$

$A = \pi r^2$

Rectangles:
$A = bh$

Formula Strips

For use in Lesson 151

English length equivalents:
1 mile = 5280 feet
1 mile = 1760 yards
1 yard = 3 feet
1 yard = 36 inches

English-Metric length equivalents:
1 inch = 2.54 cm
1 inch = 25.4 mm
1 yard = 0.91 meter
1 mile = 1.61 km

Metric-English length equivalents:
1 cm = 0.39 inch
1 meter = 1.09 yards
1 km = 0.62 mile

For use in Lesson 155

Solid geometry:

Cylinder: $V = \pi r^2 h$
$LA = 2\pi rL$
$SA = 2\pi rL + 2\pi r^2$

Pyramid: $LA = \frac{1}{2}PL$
$SA = \frac{1}{2}PL + B$

Sphere: $SA = 4\pi r^2$

For use in Lesson 156

Solid geometry:
Prism: $V = Bh$
Cone: $V = \frac{1}{3}\pi r^2 h$
$LA = \pi rL$
$SA = \pi rL + \pi r^2$

Plane geometry:
Parallelogram: $A = bh$
Triangle: $A = \frac{1}{2}bh$
Trapezoid:
$A = \frac{1}{2}(b_1 + b_2)h$

For use in Lesson 159

English-Metric liquid equivalents:
1 ounce (oz.) = 30 mL
1 quart (qt.) = 0.95 L
1 gallon (gal.) = 3.8 L

Metric-English liquid equivalents:
1 mL = 0.034 oz.
1 L = 1.06 qt.
1 L = 0.26 gal.

Weight-mass equivalents:
1 ounce (oz.) = 28.35 g
1 pound (lb.) = 0.454 kg
1 short ton (S. ton) = 907 kg
1 g = 0.035 oz.
1 kg = 2.2 lb.
1 metric ton (M. ton) = 1.1 S. ton

Formula Strips

For use on Test 16

Plane geometry:
Parallelogram: $A = bh$
Triangle: $A = \frac{1}{2}bh$
Trapezoid: $A = \frac{1}{2}(b_1 + b_2)h$

Regular polygons:
Area: $A = \frac{aP}{2}$

- -

For use on Exam 4

English length equivalents:
1 mile = 5280 feet
1 mile = 1760 yards
1 yard = 3 feet
1 yard = 36 inches

English-Metric length equivalents:
1 inch = 2.54 cm
1 inch = 25.4 mm
1 yard = 0.91 meter
1 mile = 1.61 km

Metric-English length equivalents:
1 cm = 0.39 inch
1 meter = 1.09 yards
1 km = 0.62 mile

Weight-mass equivalents:
1 ounce (oz.) = 28.35 g
1 pound (lb.) = 0.454 kg
1 short ton (S. ton) = 907 kg
1 g = 0.035 oz.
1 kg = 2.2 lb.
1 metric ton (M. ton) = 1.1 S. ton

Plane geometry:
Parallelogram: $A = bh$
Triangle: $A = \frac{1}{2}bh$
Trapezoid: $A = \frac{1}{2}(b_1 + b_2)h$

Circle: $C = 2\pi r$

$A = \pi r^2$

Regular polygon:

$A = \frac{aP}{2}$

Solid geometry:

Cylinder: $V = \pi r^2 h$
$LA = 2\pi r L$
$SA = 2\pi r L + 2\pi r^2$

Pyramid: $V = \frac{1}{3}Bh$
$LA = \frac{1}{2}PL$
$SA = \frac{1}{2}PL + B$

Sphere: $SA = 4\pi r^2$
$V = \frac{4}{3}\pi r^3$

Prism: $V = Bh$
$LA = PL$
$SA = PL + 2B$

Cone: $V = \frac{1}{3}\pi r^2 h$
$LA = \pi r L$
$SA = \pi r L + \pi r^2$

English-metric liquid equivalents:
1 ounce (oz.) = 30 mL
1 quart (qt.) = 0.95 L
1 gallon (gal.) = 3.8 L

Metric-English liquid equivalents:
1 mL = 0.034 ounce
1 L = 1.06 quarts
1 L = 0.26 gallon

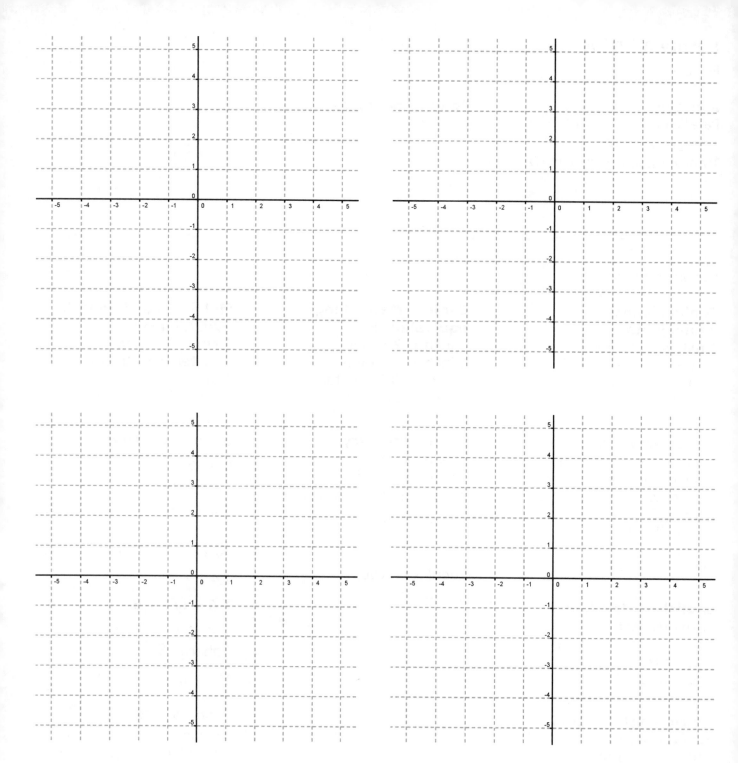

Horizons Pre-Algebra, Tests and Resources

Supplement 1: Octahedron

Directions: Cut on the solid black lines and fold on the dotted lines. Tape the edges together to form an octahedron.

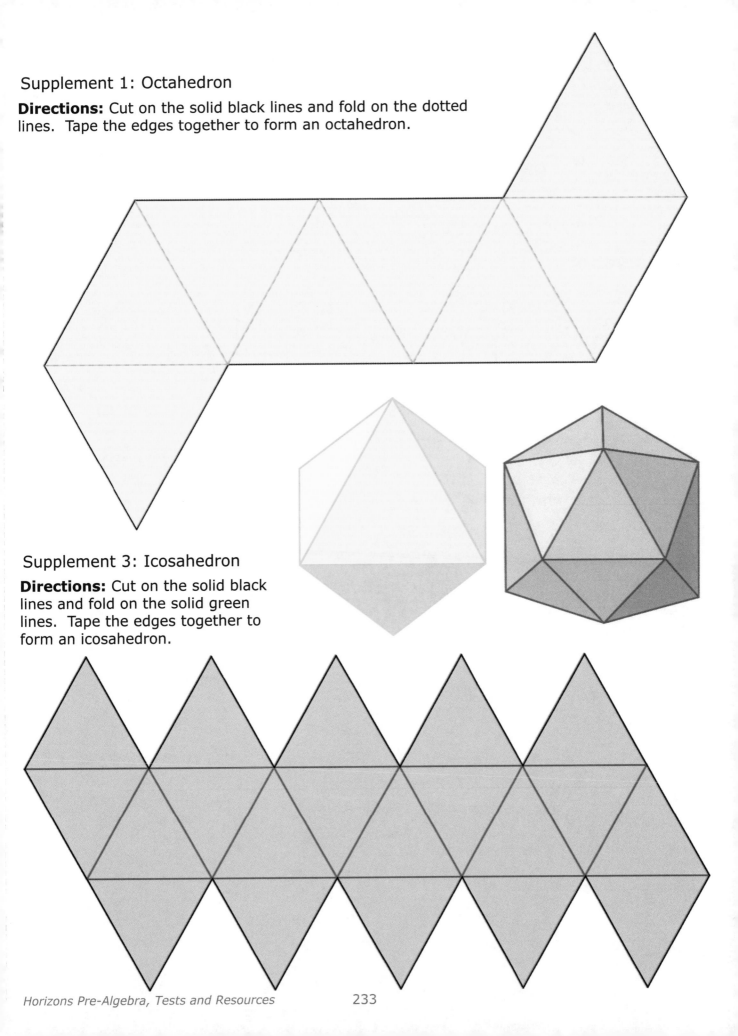

Supplement 3: Icosahedron

Directions: Cut on the solid black lines and fold on the solid green lines. Tape the edges together to form an icosahedron.

Supplement 2: Dodecahedron

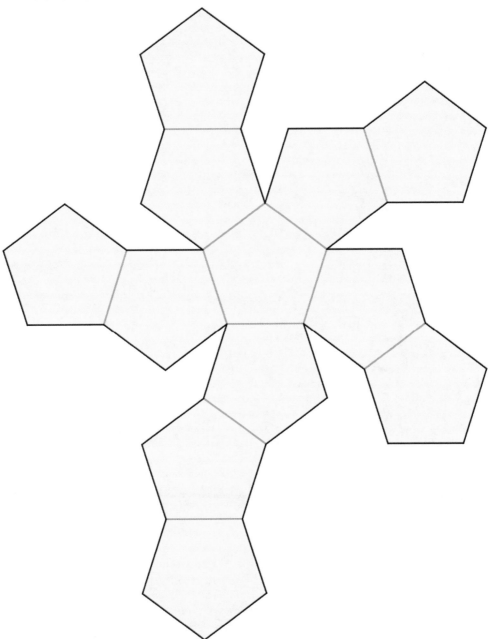

Directions: Cut on the solid black lines and fold on the solid blue lines. Tape the edges together to form a dodecahedron.

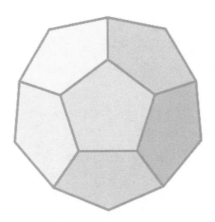

| -1 | -1 | -1 | -1 | -1 | -1 | -1 | -1 | -1 | -1 | -1 | -1 | -1 | -1 |

-x	-x	-1
-x	-x	-1
-x	-x	-1
-x	-x	-1
-x²	-x²	-1
		-1
		-1
		-1
		-1
		-1
		-1
		-1
		-1
-x²	-x²	-1
		-1
		-1
		-1